PRINCETON J

The Best of StoryLines

The Best of StoryLines

by

Hanoch Teller

Illustrated by
Getzel

New York City Publishing Company

ISBN 0-9614772-9-6

Registered in Library of Congress

12 ^{11} 10 ^{9} 8 ^{7} 6 ^{5} 4 ^{3} 2

Distributed by:
FELDHEIM PUBLISHERS
200 Airport Executive Park
Spring Valley, NY 10977

J. LEHMANN
Hebrew Booksellers
20 Cambridge Terrace
Gateshead
Tyne & Wear

Dedicated to the everlasting memory of

Manfred E. Hart ז"ל
משה בן זאב הלוי ז"ל

הלוא תדעו כי שר וגדול נפל היום הזה בישראל?   שמואל ב ג:לח
*Don't you know that a prince and a great man has
fallen this day in Israel?*
(Samuel II 3:38)

* * * * * * *

Dedicated to the eternal memory of

Isaac Urkovitch ז"ל

Who led his life with the full knowledge that:
כי אין טוב בם כי אם לשמוח ולעשות טוב בחייו. וגם כל האדם שיאכל ושתה
וראה טוב בכל עמלו מתת אלקים היא.   קהלת ג:יב,יג
*There is nothing better than to rejoice,
and to do good in life: it is the gift of God
that every man should eat and drink and enjoy the
fruits of all his labor.*
(Ecclesiastes 3:12,13)

* * * * * * *

Dedicated to the beloved memory of

Sura Urkovitch ע"ה

זרח בחשך אור לישרים חנון ורחום וצדיק...
לזכר עולם יהיה צדיק.   תהלים קיב:ד,ו
*Light rises in the darkness for the upright, the one
who is gracious, full of compassion and just...The
righteous shall be in everlasting remembrance.*
(Psalms 112:4,6)

ת.נ.צ.ב.ה.

Dedicated to the everlasting memory of

Julius Bass ז"ל

who truly personified the maxim

איזהו עשיר, השמח בחלקו.   אבות ד:א

Who is wealthy? One who rejoices with his lot.

(Pirkei Avos 4:1)

* * * * * * *

Dedicated to the loving memory of

Leah Bass ע"ה

מתהלך בתמו צדיק אשרי בניו אחריו.   משלי כ,ו

The righteous one walks with integrity so that her progeny after her can be happy.

(Proverbs 20:6)

ת.נ.צ.ב.ה.

Also by Hanoch Teller

Once Upon a Soul
Soul Survivors
'Souled!'
The Steipler Gaon
Sunset
Courtrooms of the Mind
Above the Bottom Line
Pichifkes
The Bostoner
Bridges of Steel, Ladders of Gold
"Hey, Taxi!"
Give Peace a Stance
Welcome to the Real World
13 YEARS
A Matter of Principal
О ТОМ, ЧТО НА ДУШЕ

APPROBATION FROM HAGAON HARAV
AHARON CHADASH Shlita

א׳ דסליחות התשנ"א

כבוד ידידי הנעלה והנכבד והנערץ
הרב חנוך טלר שליט"א. הנודע בחיבור ספריו הרבים
לחנך ולקרב בני ישראל ליהדות, ותורה, ומדות
טובות.

הברכה והשלום!

שגור הוא בפי יוצאי בית המוסר "דסלבודקא" אז
מיט אברייטער און א ווארעמער "שלום עליכם" קעמען
א אידייען מקרב זיין צו תורה (עם שלום עליכם חם
ולבבי אפשר לקרב אנשים לתורה). זכית הרב חנוך
נ"י בכתיבת ספריך הרבים והמבוקשים מאד, להביא
את אור היהדות ותורת המדות טובות האצורה
והגנוזה ביהדות כדוגמת מדת גמילות חסדים ואהבת
חסד שבישראל. וכן סיפורי גאונים וצדיקים ודרן
ספריך הם באים לכל קצות תבל, לקהילות מרוחקות
מיהדות שלדאבונינו נתערבו בגויים, להאיר להם את
האפילה חשכת החיים שהם חיים בהם. ולהחזירם לתוך
עם ישראל. וכל זה בהשמעת הקול היוצא מהלב "שלום
עליכם יהודים", בסגנונך הקל והכנה הנובע מלב חם
לב הדואג לכלל ישראל לזכות לכל אחד ואחד לחזור
לצור מחצבתו.

ואכן דורנו שזכה לראות בהתעוררות הגדולה מן
השמים בחלקים רבים של העם לשוב למקורות היהדות.
ורבים העוסקים במלאכת שמים זו של קירוב רחוקים
במסירות רבה. אך חלקך בזה רב מאד אם בכתיבת
ספריך הרבים או במאמרים שנכתבו על ידך בירחונים
המפורסמים בעולם. ועל כולם בנסיעותך הרבות
להרצות על היהדות בקהילות ישראל בכל קצוי תבל.
וב"ה שאני זוכים לראות את התוצאות הגדולות
ממעשיך כמו שאנו רואים מהביקוש הרב לספריך.

וברכתי שתזכה להמשיך בעבודתך עבודת הקודש זו
להפיץ תורה ויהדות לכל הפזורה באשר הם שם,
ושיהא שם שמים מתאהב על ידך. בהוקרה ובידידות,

ישיבת מיר
ירושלים

Contents

Approbation   IX
Acknowledgments   XIII
Introduction   XIX

🌸 **Spiritual Shepherds**   **23**
Heaven Scent   25
🌸 Velvel the Wagon Driver I   33
The Grudge   41
A Cool Lesson   49
The Angel of Rescue   55
An Esrog for Berditchev   61

🌸 **Precious Precepts**   **71**
Can Do   73
There's Always Room for More   87
The Judge Knot   95
A Blood Relation   101

🌸 **Honorable Mentschen**   **105**
Light in the Darkness   107
🌸 Velvel the Wagon Driver II   113
Food for Thought   121
The Bricklayer of Buchenwald   127

Stranded Simchah   133
To Save a Life   139
The Singing Soldier   143
The Mitzvah Maven   147

✻ One Good Turn   **151**
One Mitzvah Leads to Another   153
Paid in Full   159
Credit Where Credit is Due   167

✻ East Side Stories   **171**
A Stitch in Time   173
Farewell to K'vod HaTorah   195

✻ Glossary   **215**

ב״ה

Acknowledgments

I started my writing career when I was young and foolish. I am no longer young.

As these two traits are not necessarily the qualities most essential for authoring books, I understandably have a number of people to whom I owe a debt of gratitude for their help.

Marsi Tabak, in my opinion the Sovereign of Style and Redactrix Par Excellence, was with me from the inception of *StoryLines*, as she has been with virtually every other writing enterprise I have undertaken.

Getzel has done a masterful job illustrating this book. In my mind's eye, I knew exactly how Velvel, Vibel, Yingel, and Ferd looked, but it wasn't until I saw Getzel's work that I knew my mind wasn't seeing things.

Before Getzel came aboard, *SL* was privileged to have two highly talented and generous illustrators enhance each issue: Daniel Taub and Moshe Keller. During the Taub-Keller transition, two other artists graced the periodical: Toby Klerer and Sussy Flegmann. To them all: heartfelt thanks!

Sarah Scheller designed the masthead adorning every *StoryLines* issue as well as the book you are holding. S. Binyomin Ginsberg was kind enough to adapt this design for the book jacket. This volume was typeset by the devoted and talented team of Yechiel and Tybi Kapiloff, and, as always, NYC Publishing Co. brought it all to fruition.

My profound thanks to all those who — wittingly or not — told the stories that became *StoryLines*. In every instance, I have attempted to give the appropriate credit.

As with every other book I have written, there are those very deserving of mention who prefer anonymity, and I must reluctantly honor their request. Although they themselves are worthy of recognition, it is gratifying that at least their ideas and suggestions will reach the public. "What a father says to his children is not heard by the world," a humorist once noted, "but it will be heard by posterity."

Writing "Farewell to K'vod HaTorah," the biographical sketch of Reb Yaakov Joseph, was both a privilege and a grave responsibility. No one who knew the chief rabbi is alive today to offer an eyewitness account, and the testimony of "East Siders" and others who related what they had heard from their parents was rife with contradictions. I am told that a biography of the chief rabbi exists, but try as I might, I could not locate a copy of it in Israel. My research was therefore limited to an article appearing in the *Jewish Observer* by Rabbi Shmuel Singer, documentation in Rabbi Aaron Rakeffet's *The Silver Era*, and information culled by poring over the weekly and daily newspapers of the period. Special thanks to Gita Hoffman of Bar Ilan University's central library for the tip about Mayor Seth Low's commission of inquiry into responsibility for the riot at Rabbi Joseph's funeral.

In Gay Talese's short story "The Brave Tailors of Maida," a tailor avoids a predicament with some fancy needle-work. In "A Stitch in Time," a lawyer extricates himself and his client from a similar predicament — but somewhat differently, based on a true story related to me, and on my own interpretation thereof. Notwithstanding, I acknowledge that in this matter, Mr. Talese's foot-prints were there first.

In my acknowledgments, I custom-arily thank those responsible for helping and guiding me in my writing as well as in other spheres. Without their kindness, I would never have emerged or sustained myself as an author. Needless to say, both these feats have been predicated on assistance from Above, and I am pro-foundly grateful to the Almighty for en-abling me to share my twelfth book with an impressive and discriminating audi-ence.

I was raised by a mother and father who leaped at every opportunity to shower me with love. Mere acknowledgment of them cannot, I realize, begin to repay or even articulate my eternal debt.

To the sagacious scholars in Israel and abroad who have imparted of their wisdom to me, I am most obliged. If only I would be faithful to their lessons...

As a lecturer who spends a good part of the year on the road, I am most grateful to those individuals and their families all over the world who have opened their doors and their hearts to a multibook-toting vagabond. I would like to thank them all (and I beg forgiveness of anyone I have inadvertently omitted): Benjie and Sussie Brecher, Elchonen and Naomi Cohen, Rabbi Yaakov and Chevy Feitman, Bernard and Vera Garbacz, Dr. Alan and Shulamis Goldstein, Mendy and Necha-ma Itzinger, Yochanan and Sarah Kuhn-reich, Dr. Louis and Chanie Malcmacher, Dr. Mendel and Shana Monk, Reuven and Yehudis Orloff, Cheskel and Esther Paskesz, Rabbi Yitzchok and Aliza Rosen-berg, Shalom and Shaindy Siegfried, and Cantor Aryeh and Etti Subar. They and numerous other magnanimous people have provided me with asylum, often when I feared I was ready for one.

Finally, with volumes of words filling

my book shelf, I can find none to ad-
equately express my appreciation to my
wife, who shares all that I do and all that
I am.

StoryLines
Becomes a Storybook
An Introduction

he purpose of an introduction is to introduce readers to the subject of a book, but for many households the world over, *StoryLines* needs no introduction. For years, this triannual "story-letter" has heralded the arrival of Jewish festivals and brought joy and inspiration to countless homes. Now, by popular demand, some of the literary gems of *StoryLines* have been gathered in a hardcover format. This book, then, is an outgrowth of that publication, which, in turn, is an outgrowth of over a decade of writing and telling stories to youngsters and their families.

StoryLines was conceived to provide Torah-oriented literature to youngsters with limited Jewish education, as well as enjoyable, vocabulary-expanding reading to those privileged to attend yeshivos and day schools. Judging by the comments of parents and the numerous fan letters written in the inimitable scrawl of children, it is clear that we have achieved our goals.

Lest the reader conclude that *The Best of StoryLines* is exclusively a "children's book," we hasten to add that much thought and effort have gone into making this work appeal to the entire family. Rabbis and teachers, for instance, will find in these pages valuable educational material, as the feature-length story in each issue of *StoryLines* always deals with an upcoming holiday and each short story conveys Torah values.

When I signed off *"Hey, Taxi!"* with a fond farewell, noting that it was to be my final volume of "soul stories," I never imagined that one little sentence buried in the middle of an introduction would elicit a virtual outcry of protest. Although it was not my intention, word leaked out — faster than radiation from a reactor — that I was imbedding my pen deep in mothballs.

I was deeply touched by the calls for

a retraction. I hope a "clarification" of how this book differs from my other volumes will suffice.

More than any of my other works, *SL* was designed for children, with their needs and tastes in mind. Children play a primary role in Jewish life: they are there when we wake up and when we go to sleep, and in between, even when they aren't there, they're there — on our minds, and sometimes on our nerves. They are a major source of happiness, inspiration, solace, guilt, love, frustration, and perspective on our lives. Accordingly, their education and enjoyment should not be neglected. What better way to address the two than in a collection of stories that can be read either by them or to them and discussed in family forums.

"Velvel the Wagon Driver" is a regular *StoryLines* feature. The protagonists are Velvel of Schnitzelberg, of course, Vibel, Yingel, and the lovably cynical Ferd. (Respectively, the names are Yiddish for wolf, wife, boy, and horse.) A host of their happy holiday comic strips have been reproduced here in full color by the talented Getzel, and their hilarious escapades enhance this book.

In a break with tradition, I have adopted the policy laid down in manuals of writing style for using italics, i.e., foreign words are italicized only if they do *not* appear in an English-language dictionary. In recent years, words such as mitzvah, seder, Shabbos, yeshivah, etc., have found their way into Webster's.

Like most of my books, *The Best of StoryLines* is an anthology of stories based on actual incidents. Often, either to protect the privacy of the protagonists or to emphasize a certain message contained therein, the stories have been modified, but their essential truth remains.

Happy reading!

יהיו לרצון אמרי פי . . .

Hanoch Teller
Jerusalem תו״ב
Erev Rosh HaShanah 5752
September 1991

SPIRITUAL SHEPHERDS

Heaven Scent

After the passing of the famed Reb Yissachar, the Jews of Nikolsburg entered a period of deep mourning. Who would replace their beloved Rebbe? Who would inspire and guide them? Little did they know that one of the giants of chassidic Jewry would soon assume the mantle of leadership within their community.

To their delight, these chassidim discovered that none other than the holy and most righteous Reb Shmelke of Nikolsburg, disciple of the Maggid of Mezritch and master of Reb Moshe Leib of Sassov, was to become their spiritual leader. A grand reception was held in honor of the arrival of Reb Shmelke, ending with a tour of Reb Yissachar's house, which would now become his home.

Reb Shmelke was led through the spacious, orderly house, but as he passed from one room to the next, he seemed distracted. He barely paid attention to the tour that he was given and when it was over he announced why: "There is a most remarkable aroma coming from this house, and I am certain that it emanates from some beautiful deed performed here."

Reb Shmelke was driven to find the source of the scent. For a week he searched for the answer. He asked kinfolk and townsfolk, absolutely anyone who had had dealings with Reb Yissachar, but no one could recall anything out of the ordinary.

One day, as Reb Shmelke was walking down the road, a gentile woman approached him. "Rabbi," she said in a low, hesitant voice, "I understand that you wish to discover a beautiful deed per-

formed by the previous rabbi of Nikolsburg. Now, I don't know if this is the
incident you are looking for, but allow me
to recount it to you nonetheless."

Reb Shmelke leaned against the wall
and listened carefully as the woman began to tell her tale:

"I was hired as a maid in Reb Yissachar's home. My first day at work was
Passover eve and no sooner had I arrived
that day than the rabbi and his wife and
older children left for the market, leaving me alone to tend the babies. About
an hour after they had gone, the children
awoke and started to cry.

"I went into the kitchen to prepare
something for them to eat, but I couldn't
find a thing! Apparently the Passover
provisions had not yet arrived, and all
the shelves and pantries were bare. The
babies began to scream and I didn't
know what to do. I searched high and
low until finally, at the bottom of the
clothes closet in the master's bedroom, I
found a box containing some large,
round crackers."

Reb Shmelke understood what those
"crackers" were. He also understood how
much pain, effort and money Reb Yissachar had put into getting them. He had

undoubtedly gone to the field and over-
seen the harvest, making sure that no
water came into contact with the wheat.
He then had personally ground the grain
and hauled it to the bakery, where he
had rolled up his sleeves and kneaded,
flattened, and baked the *shmurah matzos.* In short, they had cost him dearly,
both in energy and in expense.

"Later that morning," the maid continued, "everyone returned and immediately began preparing for the holiday.
The Rebbetzin and her children busily
set the table for the seder. They brought
out the most beautiful china and silver-
ware they owned, and lovingly placed
them on the table. Crystal wine goblets
and linen napkins graced every setting,
creating an atmosphere of royalty and
grandeur not only in the dining room but
throughout the sparklingly clean house.

"The children began to place pillows
on the chairs as the Rebbetzin took a
beautifully decorated seder plate from
the very same box in which the Passover
china had been stored. In minutes she
had filled it with a roasted shank bone
and a roasted egg, stalks of green bitter
herbs, a generous serving of wine-red
charoses, and fresh, crisp parsley.

"The hour was late. Reb Yissachar was about to leave for synagogue but first he hauled a crate of wine bottles into the dining room and placed them near his seat. The smell of golden chicken soup and fluffy matzah balls filled the home.

"As Reb Yissachar inspected the dining room, a smile of satisfaction spread across his face. Everything but the matzah had been placed on the table, which by now bore every sign of a banquet setting fit for a king.

"Suddenly, a bitter cry rent the air. Reb Yissachar ran to the bedroom where the commotion was coming from. By the time he arrived, all the children were shrieking and shouting. Moments later, both parents and children were scurrying about the house, searching everywhere for what was apparently a most precious object.

"I had never seen such distress overcome a family before. It was then that I realized my mistake. Gathering all the courage I had, I approached Reb Yissachar with great trepidation. I was trembling, 'Excuse me, sir,' I said, my voice quavering, 'but while you were out this morning and I was here all alone, I had to feed the children. I just couldn't find anything to give them until I discovered those large, oval crackers in the bottom of the clothes closet in the bedroom.'

"A long and tense silence filled the room as the meaning of my words was grasped. Reb Yissachar seemed to be lost in thought, and then he asked me to repeat what I had said. I was even more frightened now and could hardly speak, but somehow I repeated that I had fed the crackers to the children.

"No sooner had I finished my confession than Reb Yissachar called out to his wife without a trace of anger, tension or even sadness, 'Please bring some ordinary matzos so that we can conduct the seder.' Then he turned to me and said: 'Thank you for taking such good care of my children.'"

Reb Shmelke now understood where that wonderful aroma came from. The moment Reb Yissachar had realized that there was nothing whatsoever that he could do about the loss of his dear *shmurah matzos* — the labor of his love on which he had spent so much time, energy and money — he put the entire episode behind him. After all, why ruin the holiday spirit with a self-indulgent display of temper?

Heard from: Grand Rabbi Levi Yitzchak Horowitz

SUKKOS IN SCHNITZELBERG...
THE COLDEST SUKKOS IN MEMORY

VELVEL HAS A VISITOR...
COUSIN ITZIK FROM ICICLEBERG

VELVEL, VIBEL AND YINGEL ARE [RI]DING HOME TO [S]CHNITZELBERG [W]ITH A WAGON-LOAD OF POTATOES...

WHY ARE WE GOING SO SLOW?

YINGEL, IT'S HARD ON FERD WHO HAS TO PULL SUCH A HEAVY LOAD.

IT SURE IS...

BUT VELVEL, IT'S GETTING DARK. ISN'T THIS ROAD DANGEROUS AT NIGHT?

IT WAS REAL NICE OF THE FARMER TO GIVE ME MY OWN JUG OF OIL FOR THE MENORAH.

YES, BUT SINCE WE'RE DOING A MITZVA - BRINGING POTATOES SO EVERYONE CAN HAVE LATKES FOR CHANUKA — NO HARM WILL COME TO US.

The Grudge

he temperature was well below freezing, not unusual for a Russian winter. Frigid gusts of wind blew through even the warmest clothing and everyone sought shelter indoors, preferably around a nice, hot stove.

One man, however, braved the cold. He was Rabbi Chaim Soloveitchik, also known as Reb Chaim Brisker (because he was a rabbi in the Lithuanian town of Brisk), who waited at the railroad station for the train to take him home.

That Rabbi Soloveitchik was the towering rabbinic figure of Lithuanian Jewry was beyond question. Indeed, so sharp and penetrating was his mind that fellow

Jews held him in absolute awe.

Yet only a keen eye would have recognized one of the world's most outstanding Torah scholars standing on the train platform that morning, for Reb Chaim was as humble as he was brilliant. Whenever he traveled, Rabbi Soloveitchik wore the common clothing typical of a plain, poor Jew of eighty years ago in that region. His formal rabbinic coat was reserved for other occasions.

In those days (and still today in Europe) the cars of a train were divided into different "classes": first class, second class, and so on. Reb Chaim traveled in the lowest class, the least expensive section where the poorest passengers crowded into the most cramped train compartments.

When the train heading for Brisk arrived at the station, Reb Chaim searched through these compartments for a vacant seat. The only one available was alongside three other Jews who were playing cards and were obviously drunk. The three were very pleased when Reb Chaim joined them, not because they recognized their special guest but because they would now have a foursome for their card game.

Obviously, Rabbi Chaim Soloveitchik had no interest in cavorting with a bunch of drunkards, much less in engaging in a card game, so he politely but firmly declined their offer.

"Come on, old man," one of them said, slapping Reb Chaim on the back. "Let us deal you in!"

Naturally, Reb Chaim still refused.

"Listen here, Pops," another of the group addressed the newcomer in a threatening voice, "if you won't play cards with us, we'll throw you out of this compartment and you'll find yourself out in the cold."

Even this threat failed to change Rabbi Soloveitchik's mind and he was promptly banished to the cold corridor of the speeding train.

When the train arrived in Brisk, a large crowd was waiting to greet Reb Chaim. The card players were too drunk to realize exactly what they had done wrong, but they were sober enough to understand that they had made a big mistake.

The next day they discovered to their horror that they had insulted none other than the most famous rabbi of the period, Rabbi Chaim Soloveitchik. They shuddered at the thought. Clearly they would have to beg his forgiveness, but in light of their cruelty, they were ashamed to approach him. Finally, the three hit upon the idea of choosing one of them to represent the others, so they cast lots and a delegate was selected.

As the fellow entered Reb Chaim's office, he trembled with fright. He had trouble maintaining his balance because his legs were quivering, and even more trouble finding his tongue.

"R... R... Reb Ch... Chaim," he stammered nervously, "we are soooo sorry. We didn't realize that it was you. Please understand that we were hopelessly drunk — and we'd only been drinking to keep warm, of course — so we didn't know what we were doing. We would never have thrown you out of the compartment if we had been in our right minds. Please, please forgive us! Look, I've even brought a donation for your yeshivah," he hastened to add, fumbling in his pockets for some money.

But he didn't get very far before Reb Chaim flatly responded, "I cannot forgive you," and resumed learning.

The man, who had been trembling to begin with, now began to shake from head to toe. He quickly backed out of the room and hurried to join his friends outside and report the sad news.

Half a year later, it was *erev Rosh Ha-Shanah.* Since the last thing any Jew wants is to begin the New Year with a great rabbi holding something against him, the three card players decided that they should all go together to beg Rabbi Soloveitchik's forgiveness. They were certain that the approach of Rosh Ha-Shanah would put Reb Chaim in a conciliatory mood.

But they were mistaken. Even after they politely pleaded their case, Rabbi Soloveitchik responded just as he had before: "I cannot forgive you."

Ten days later was *erev Yom Kippur.* It is well known that before Yom Kippur, there is a special mitzvah to pardon all personal affronts and bear no grudges. This would also be the trio's third attempt at appeasement, so they were sure that this time, as required by Jewish law, Reb Chaim would forgive them.

However, the very minute they entered Reb Chaim's office, their confidence disappeared; clearly, it wasn't going to be so simple after all. Once again, they begged Reb Chaim to pardon them. "We'll do whatever you say," they promised.

Unmoved, Rabbi Soloveitchik simply reiterated, "I cannot forgive you."

Not knowing what to do with themselves, the three shuffled miserably out of the rabbi's office.

In desperation they turned to Reb Velvel, Rabbi Soloveitchik's son, for help. They retold the entire story of the train ride, and of how Reb Chaim had rebuffed them although they'd pleaded with him three times in a row.

Reb Velvel couldn't believe his ears. His father had never been one to hold a grudge; in fact, he was always the very first to forgive. Perplexed, Reb Velvel offered to approach him on the trio's behalf.

When he did, he found that Reb Chaim's by-now familiar refrain had not changed. "I cannot forgive them!" his father told him. But Reb Velvel noticed the emphasis on the first word: "*I* cannot forgive them!"

"They thought I was a plain, simple Jew," Reb Chaim explained, "and that's why they acted the way they did. Had they known who I was, I'm certain they would never have behaved so heartlessly. The insult, therefore, was not directed at *me* so *I* cannot forgive them. Their only hope of atonement lies in begging forgiveness from plain, simple Jews and in changing their attitude toward their humble brethren."

Heard from: Joseph Telushkin

A Cool Lesson

Outside it was as cold as the frozen tundra. Snow covered everything, and any depression in the street where water had once collected was now a slab of ice. The chimneys and large-bellied ovens that were a fixture in every dwelling in town were working around the clock in their battle against the cold. Yes, the Russian winter felt very much at home in Lodz.

No sooner had the esteemed rabbi of the town, Rabbi Eliyahu Chaim Meisel, returned from the synagogue than he set out again for the home of the wealthiest Jew in all of Lodz.

Rabbi Meisel rarely visited people in

the middle of the week, unless it was to pay a condolence call, visit the sick, or otherwise perform his communal and religious duties. Accordingly, Asher Steinfeld, Lodz's most successful merchant, was both surprised and honored to have the rabbi knock on his door, despite the lateness of the hour.

"Rabbi, won't you please come in?" Steinfeld offered generously, sweeping his hand in the direction of his spacious, well-heated living room.

A blizzard was brewing outside, the snow falling thickly and the frigid wind howling, making shutters rattle and bones quiver. Rabbi Meisel, however, did not seem the least bit concerned about the weather. Instead, planting his foot in the open doorway, he began to carry on a very casual conversation. "Good evening, Reb Asher, and how is your little boy getting along in school?"

"Please, please, won't you come in? I'm sure we'd both be happier chatting in front of a roaring fire."

The rabbi either didn't hear or chose to ignore his host's offer. "Is he studying as well as he should be?" he persisted.

"Oh... er... yes," Steinfeld answered, rubbing his hands together and flapping his arms to promote circulation.

"And how is your older daughter getting on?" the rabbi probed.

"Please, honorable Rabbi, come inside," Steinfeld begged, his ears pink and his nose bright red. By now, he was practically jumping up and down to keep from freezing.

Yet Rabbi Meisel doggedly continued with his small talk. "Do your in-laws plan to join you again this year for Purim?"

Asher Steinfeld's lips were purple and his teeth were chattering. No wonder he couldn't express himself, for his words froze before leaving his mouth. All he could do was gesture towards his toasty living room, which had meanwhile cooled down considerably

"Ahh, Mr. Steinfeld," the rabbi said with warmth in his voice and not a hint of chill in his demeanor, "that is precisely why I have come to visit you on this typically frosty winter night. The boys in the yeshivah are chilled to the bone! Their clothing is inadequate not only for the outdoors but for the unheated indoors of the yeshivah.

"As diligent as they are, they can hardly concentrate while their bodies are freezing from the cold. They have no collars to pull up, no mittens to wear, and no fur hats to cover their ears. The words of Torah they recite vaporize and hang in the air like clouds of steam in a bathhouse.

"Mr. Steinfeld, I hope you now understand why I have exposed you to the frigid weather for these last few minutes. How could I plead the cause of freezing yeshivah students while sitting next to your fireplace in the warmth of your home? Perhaps now you'll be moved to give generously, to donate as only one who truly appreciates another's plight can."

The merchant was only too happy to comply.

Heard from: Rabbi Avigdor Nebanzahl

The Angel of Rescue

One of the most glorious chapters in our People's history is reserved for a single Englishman: Dr. Solomon Schonfeld. Known to some as the "Angel of Rescue" and to others simply as "Father," he was both to thousands of our brethren trapped by the Nazis and abandoned by the world at large.

Every Jew that Dr. Schonfeld saved was a story unto himself, a gripping tale filled with drama and heroics. Time and again, Dr. Schonfeld endangered his freedom and even his life to help the victims of war, placing the welfare of others above his own. No matter how great the risk or how improbable the odds, nothing could deter this outstanding statesman and rescue worker.

A rabbi by profession, Dr. Schonfeld somehow managed to get hold of a British Army uniform, which he wore in order to provide himself with an aura of authority. In actuality, however, he needed no impressive regalia to win people's confidence. The rabbi's clear, bright eyes, his height and bearing, together with his forthright manner of speech always earned him attention and respect.

When World War II finally ended in 1945, the battle to save Jewish lives — physically and spiritually — had hardly begun for Dr. Schonfeld. There were still thousands of Jews, primarily orphaned children, who had no home to return to and no family members left alive.

With determination and originality as his only weapons, the rabbi fought for the emigration of every Jewish soul marooned on Europe's blood-drenched soil. Equally concerned that the orphans be raised in a warm, Jewish environment, Dr. Schonfeld invested unlimited time and energy in seeking loving families to adopt them.

One typical story from this period involves a fellow who sought Dr. Schonfeld's aid in rescuing a young relative stranded in Europe. Because the rabbi was so incredibly busy, the only time he could schedule a meeting was at 3:00 in the morning. But at least at that hour, the petitioner was certain, he would have Rabbi Schonfeld's undivided attention.

Imagine his surprise when he found dozens of people ahead of him on line that morning! When his turn finally came, Dr. Schonfeld had his hair cut as he listened carefully and took notes. And when the fellow left, he saw someone preparing the rabbi's "supper."

As if this unparalleled selflessness weren't enough, whenever Dr. Schonfeld could not find an appropriate family to adopt an orphan, he would gather the refugee under his own protective wings!

During one of the rabbi's trips to Europe after the war, he received a message that the British ambassador in Prague was looking for him. Dr. Schonfeld reported to the embassy the next morning and was greeted by a very

angry-looking official.

"Are you the Dr. Schonfeld who has been arranging the 'children's transports'?" he demanded.

"Yes, I am," Dr. Schonfeld replied.

"Are you not a member of the clergy?" the ambassador pressed.

"That is true," he nodded.

"Well, then, I'll have you know that yesterday a woman came to see me, requesting permission to visit her son in England. It soon became clear to me that her son had left for Britain in one of your transports.

"It just so happens," the ambassador went on, "that the British government issues visas for the children on your transports on the assumption that they are orphans. But if a woman wishes to visit her son, then surely the child is *not* an orphan! You are therefore guilty of committing a disgraceful crime by deceiving us. A member of the clergy should know better than to lie!"

Dr. Schonfeld rose to his full height. "Mr. Ambassador," he countered forcefully, banging his hand down on the desk with a loud clap, "if there is one Jewish child left in all of Europe whose mother is still alive, will you hold it against all the others?"

The tragic truth of Dr. Schonfeld's words quickly registered with the British official and he immediately regretted his outburst. Indeed, his cold, blue eyes, which moments before had been filled with anger, now filled with tears.

According to Dr. Schonfeld, this very ambassador would yet compensate for his mistake. He ended up providing the Angel of Rescue with more visas for Jews than any other clerk in the British Foreign Office.

Heard from: Rabbi Abba Dunner

An Esrog for Berditchev

When it came to securing a beautiful *esrog* for Sukkos, no one was more particular than the famous and saintly Reb Levi Yitzchak of Berditchev. Months before the holiday season, he would begin his search for an *esrog* that was truly *mehudar*.

By and large, *esrogim* are grown in Eretz Yisrael and shipped all over the world. One year, however, the ship carrying the precious cargo from the Holy Land to Berditchev never arrived. Distraught, Reb Levi Yitzchak — also known as the Berditchever Rebbe — sent messengers to all the outlying areas, hoping

that they would discover an *esrog* somewhere in their travels. But the messengers returned emptyhanded. Their efforts
had borne no fruit.

One week before Rosh HaShanah —
only three weeks until Sukkos — there
was still no hope in sight. So the Rebbe
sent out a new group of messengers,
instructing them to bring back an *esrog*
— any *esrog* — at any price! But their
mission, too, was a failure.

On Yom Kippur, the Rebbe implored
the Almighty to allow him to fulfill this
mitzvah as he always had. "Master of the
Universe, we wish to obey Your command," he cried, "but there isn't a single
esrog in all of Berditchev or the surrounding countryside!"

Just before the *Ne'ilah* service, Reb
Levi Yitzchak issued a moving plea to the
hundreds of worshippers gathered in his
shul: "I ask each one of you to take to
the streets tomorrow, stop any Jewish
wagon driver you see, and inquire
whether he has an *esrog*. We must spare
no effort to fulfill Almighty's commandments!"

This was followed by a unique prayer
he had composed himself:

"*Ribbono Shel Olam, l'ommer machen a*

bayt — Master of the Universe, let us make a deal. I will give You my sins, transgressions, and errors, and You will give me children, life, and sustenance.

"The Greeks contend that their god is the Lord, but I disagree.

"The Romans contend that their god is the Lord, but I disagree.

"The Indians contend that their god is the Lord, but I disagree.

"And the Russians contend that there *is* no God, but I, Levi Yitzchak ben Sarah Sushah, say, '*Yisgadeil viyiskadeish Shemei rabba...* Glorified and sanctified be God's great name...'"

The next day, as per the Rebbe's instructions, one of his chassidim at the northern entrance to Berditchev accosted Berel the spice merchant who was returning home from the summer fair. Lo and behold, Berel had an *esrog*, a very beautiful one... but he had no interest in parting with it. Anxious to return to his family, he didn't appreciate being buttonholed and questioned by a persistent chassid.

"I've been away from my family for the entire summer," the merchant argued. "I've earned plenty of money, *baruch Hashem,* so none of your offers can tempt me. This little *esrog* will be the highlight of my family's Sukkos; it will be our *simchas Yom Tov.*"

But the chassid was determined to succeed in his mission; he just would not take "no" for an answer.

Eventually, after a lengthy debate, Berel was brought to the court of the Berditchever Rebbe and offered a very handsome price for his *esrog.* Still the merchant refused.

"But you haven't heard my final offer yet," Reb Levi Yitzchak proposed in a soft voice.

Berel was about to raise his hand to indicate that he would not change his mind for any sum of money, but before he managed to convey this message, the Rebbe dropped his bombshell: "Sell me your *esrog* in exchange for my portion in the World to Come."

The Rebbe's offer was astounding! As a businessman, Berel recognized a terrific deal when he heard one, and this was one proposition no Jew could afford to pass up. After all, Reb Levi Yitzchak's piety was legendary and there was no doubt at all that a special place of honor awaited him in the World to Come.

The Rebbe explained his proposal, making the deal sound even more tempting: "We wouldn't want you to be lacking an *esrog* for Yom Tov, so you will be our guest for the holiday, and you may use the *esrog* just like every other Jew in Berditchev."

The merchant immediately gave his consent and sent word to his family. He was then given comfortable accommodations in the home of one of the Rebbe's chassidim.

On the first night of Sukkos — when the Torah commands us to eat in a sukkah — Berel joined Berditchev's chassidim for evening prayers in the shul. The service was moving and was chanted with an enthusiasm and an intensity that he had never experienced before. He returned home from shul extremely inspired and looking forward to the festive meal he was about to enjoy.

But when he walked through the door, his host turned to him and said, "You may not eat in our sukkah."

The merchant could not believe his ears!

"We will not deny you food," the host assured him, "but you may not enter our sukkah to eat it."

Angry and deeply offended, Berel stormed out of the house, vowing never to return to such an ungracious host. But when he knocked on the door of a neighbor and asked if he could join him in his sukkah, to his total astonishment, this fellow, too, refused.

He tried door after door, house after house, but every chassid in Berditchev turned him away. Berel was beside himself with resentment and frustration. "What an evil town of sinners!" he thought to himself. "Imagine denying a fellow Jew permission to eat in a sukkah!"

It was already after midnight and the merchant was as hungry as he was furious. In desperation, he approached a Jewish family on the other side of town and begged to be let in.

This resident refused him, too, although not as rudely as the others. He also hinted that the Berditchever Rebbe was behind the ban on Berel. Enraged, Berel made a beeline for Reb Levi Yitzchak's house and burst through the door.

"What have you done to me?" the businessman snarled through clenched teeth, confronting the Rebbe. "Don't I have the right to fulfill the mitzvah of eating in a sukkah on the first night of Sukkos?"

"You certainly do," the Rebbe replied, "...provided that you sell me back my World to Come."

"What?!" Berel smacked his palms together as he lost all control of his temper. "You," he accused, "are supposed to be the pious Reb Levi Yitzchak of Berditchev, the leader and advocate of the Jewish People. But look how low you have stooped, tricking me into abandoning my family and selling my *esrog* under false pretenses!"

"My dear friend," the Rebbe said calmly, "my World to Come is still yours, and our deal is still a deal. However, if you wish to eat in a sukkah tonight, you will have to sell it back to me."

The businessman paced back and forth, thinking over his terrible problem. On the one hand, he had only remained in Berditchev in order to use the *esrog* he had sold for the Rebbe's World to Come. On the other hand, every year of his life — in stormy wind, pouring rain, or frosty snow — he had eaten in a suk-kah, or at least recited kiddush there, on the first night of Sukkos.

Berel thought it over again and again. Finally, he concluded that no matter what he stood to lose, he had to do what was right: he had to eat in a suk-kah the first night of Sukkos.

"Very well," the businessman responded with a heavy heart, "I will resell you your portion in the World to Come in exchange for a meal in a sukkah."

Reb Levi Yitzchak breathed a deep sigh of relief and offered Berel a warm embrace — and an explanation:

"In my eagerness to secure an *esrog* for my People, I gave away my World to Come. Once I had made the deal, however, I deeply regretted my decision, for how could I — how dare I — give away something so precious to a person who might have done nothing to earn it? After all, did you not refuse at first to share your *esrog* with the Jews of Berditchev, knowing full well that without it we would all have been deprived of the mitzvah?

"But now that I see you have passed this difficult trial of faith and opted to do what is right, it is clear that you are truly deserving of my World to Come.

"And now, Reb Berel, please come into my sukkah, where it will be my honor to personally serve you."

Heard from: Rabbi Yosef Zeinwerth

PRECIOUS PRECEPTS

Can Do

Trayfuls of jelly doughnuts, platters overflowing with *latkes*, drinks galore, a lively band, friendly company — this party wasn't missing a single ingredient. But the best element of all, the aspect that elevated it from a party into a celebration, was the atmosphere.

The hundreds of Russian immigrants attending the affair had never participated in a *simchah shel mitzvah* before. When they had seen the announcement in a Russian-language newspaper and on billboards in their neighborhoods, what had attracted them was not the fact that it was a Chanukah party, but that admission to the event was free. And so they came, they and their families and their neighbors and their friends — hundreds more than had been anticipated — but the boys of the Riets Yeshivah in New York were ready for them.

First, the yeshivah's Russian students put on a play and acted out the story of Chanukah in their native language, enabling their countrymen to appreciate what it was that they were celebrating. Indeed, now that the reason for the revelry was understood, the participants added to the joy by dancing the "*kazatzka*" and singing "The Song of the Volga Boatmen." And yet... and yet, a question mark seemed to hover over the festivities.

Every Russian in the room had, to a greater or lesser degree, benefited from the American Jewish community's kindness and generosity, but none had ever been treated to such a sumptuous spread. Most remarkably, it was hosted not by any organization or recognized establishment, but by a motley group of young yeshivah students.

Having been raised in an environment where nothing happened by chance and everything was completely calculated, the Russians were understandably curious to know who was behind the event. Who was it who had so earnestly wanted to introduce Chanukah into their lives? The answer was not long in coming.

One of the yeshivah students, a short fellow with glasses and a black hat pushed all the way to the back of his head, leaped onto a table and a hush fell over the audience. "As you now know," the boy began without any formal introduction, "the story of Chanukah teaches how a few God-fearing Jews were able to defeat the mighty Greek-Syrian armies. But at the very heart of the story is a little jug of oil that brought joy not only to the Jews who presided over the rededication of the Temple, but to Jews in every generation ever since...

"Likewise, tonight's event is brought to you by the help of God and," he lifted up for everyone to see, "a little can of Diet Coke."

Instantly, the students began to cheer and applaud wildly.

You must wonder, dear Reader, how a simple aluminum can of soda could bring about such a gala event. Well, it's a long story, one that began a few months before Chanukah in the mythical kingdom of Riets.

The subjects of the kingdom were by and large a decent sort. They learned Torah and observed its precepts faithfully, they performed acts of loving-kindness and gave charity, and thrice daily they repaired to the sanctuary to worship their Creator. One day, however, their peaceful kingdom was invaded by a mighty army of deliverymen and technicians who left in their wake a device that came to dominate the hallowed halls of the Riets dormitory: it was called Soda Machine.

Soon, the young citizens of the kingdom began to make frequent pilgrimages to Soda Machine, offering monetary contributions in exchange for sweet libations. Soda Machine became such an irresistible temptation that the faithful often exceeded their normal tithe of pocket money allowances and even went into debt to acquire more and more of Soda Machine's heady elixir.

Yet the students' ardent offerings did not always find favor in Soda Machine's eyes. From time to time, it merely accepted the monetary offering but presented no sweet libation. On such occasions, pilgrims could become quite enraged, pounding, kicking, and even shaking Soda Machine with all their might.

On the whole, however, the device was treated with great respect. In fact, the people of Riets could no longer remember a time when Soda Machine had not been a part of their lives. Although they still learned Torah and worshipped their Creator, many were also so faithful to Soda Machine that the coins they regularly fed into the device were no longer available for charitable causes. The mitzvah of giving *tzedakah* was nearly forgotten... until Izzy Wolf came along, a modern-day "redeemer" — in more ways than one.

Our hero was not a man of means but he wanted to contribute *tzedakah* in a meaningful way and, although he hadn't actually planned it at the time, to help protect the environment as well. Now, everyone knows that empty aluminum soda cans may be redeemed for cash at the local supermarket. Everyone also knows that few people bother to take advantage of this offer.

Izzy Wolf viewed the redemption option as an opportunity to involve his somewhat wayward fellow denizens of the Riets Yeshivah in a *tzedakah* project — one that would literally cost them nothing. Accordingly, right after Rosh HaShanah, Izzy came up with a "redemption offer" of his own. He hauled a large, empty carton out of the trash and affixed a sign to it that read: "DUMP YOUR SODA CANS HERE. ALL PROCEEDS TO *TZE-DAKAH*."

The next morning, he awoke to find the carton filled to overflowing with soda cans. At six-and-a-half cents per, the twenty-seven cans didn't amount to much, but then again, the project was just a few hours old. By the end of the week, which not coincidentally happened to be *Asseres Yemei Teshuvah*, $20 had been raised.

Izzy's roommate Abie, a born businessman, realized immediately that if the project were to spread to every floor of the dormitory and every corner of the yeshivah, the "take" for *tzedakah* would dwarf the initial $20 figure.

Alas, the royal administrators of Riets were somewhat less than enthusiastic. They visualized overflowing cartons and litter strewn about the hallways, creating an unseemly health hazard. Izzy and Abie promised to empty the cartons regularly, but the powers that be remained skeptical. Such an ambitious project, they asserted, required the involvement of a more mature, responsible authority than just two well-meaning *bachurim.*

Thus was born the "Riets Philanthropic Society." It was a rather august name for two teenage yeshivah kids, but Abie and Izzy took their project seriously, awarding it all the respect a *tzedakah* enterprise deserves. They even saw to it that the Society became an official chartered organization, complete with a constitution, and elections (naturally, Abie and Izzy initially served as co-presidents).

One of the nicest things about the Riets Philanthropic Society was that it truly was philanthropic, not only in its distribution of funds and goods to worthy causes, but in its grass-roots operation. Dozens and, at times, hundreds of volunteers pitched in with the project, clearing away the boxes (which later became bins) every Friday afternoon and shlepping the contents to the supermarket, where the cans were redeemed for cash. These funds in turn were bartered for meals (at a very special rate worked out with the yeshivah's cafeteria), which in turn were delivered before Shabbos to lonely, elderly Jewish residents of the neighborhood. To these neglected souls, the meal program — and the wholesome company who delivered it — was like manna from Heaven.

As the project continued, something peculiar happened. Either the students became a lot thirstier, or they got a kick out of pitching empty cans into the large Philanthropic Society bins, or, most likely, the advent of midterm exams generated irresistible nocturnal cravings for dextrose and caffeine. Whatever the cause, the number of cans deposited tripled as a result!

Izzy and Abie's room, where the full bins were stored until they were taken every Friday to the supermarket, underwent a metamorphosis. Once a humble dormitory facility, it now became a major storage center. There were cans under the beds, in the closets, on top of the closets, blocking the window, and piled, stacked, and strewn all over the floor.

Indeed, one night when Izzy retired to his room, he couldn't find his roommate! "Abie, oh Abie, where are you?" he cried. He thought he heard him, but he couldn't find him. Abie's orthodontia usually made him stand out in a crowd, but in that room, well, his "aluminum siding" provided complete camouflage.

After repeated calls, Izzy discerned a faint rustling amid the eerily creaking wall of heavy metal. He feared the worst.

"Don't worry, buddy! I'll save you!" he reassured his partner in philanthropy and bravely began to slice through the *Slice* and punch through the *Punch*. Suddenly a barricade of *Sprite* began a spritely avalanche, peppering Izzy with *Dr. Peppers* and creaming him with *Hoffman Cream Sodas.*

Abie, not much the worse for having been submerged under seven hefty *Hefty* bags of *Seven-Up*, emerged at last for air. He didn't seem to have enjoyed his caper across *Canada Dry.* "Chooth!" he lisped through the pop-tops entangled in his bicuspids. "Either the canth go, or I go!"

Izzy stalled for time, considering his options, but it was clear that if he wanted to keep both his roommate *and* the cans, a new solution was required.

So the Philanthropic Society co-presidents clangorously navigated their way through the hallways, treacherous straits mined with hundreds of cans that had escaped and scattered the moment their dorm-room door was opened. The presidium proceeded to the suite of the dorm supervisor, where, in the name of liberty, justice, and simple sanity, the dynamic duo demanded that they be allocated a storage room for their weekly haul of cans. Permission was duly granted and minutes later, a brigade of tin soldiers (composed of Izzy, Abie, and a floorful of grateful students) toted, tossed, and transported mountain ranges of soda cans to their new accommodations.

That Friday, the caravan of can-transport vehicles bearing the goods and their redeemers spanned two city blocks and the proceeds were well into the triple digits. Izzy was delighted, of course, but he couldn't help feeling that there had to be an easier way to cash in the cans than trudging to the supermarket and manually loading 7,500 of them — one at a time — into a hopper. Abie was ready to can the whole project when suddenly his business-honed mind took a dazzling leap of logic.

Realizing that he was now dealing with a genuine business venture, Abie called up the Coca-Cola Bottling Co., which owned the major soda concession at the yeshivah, and Coke readily agreed to send down a truck every Friday afternoon. That left the Riets Philanthropic Society with the relatively simple task of sorting, separating and cleaning the cans prior to pickup, an undertaking performed late Thursday nights by a dedicated crew of volunteers.

As midterm cramming moved into high gear, revenues soared. Consequently, the Society's board of directors decided to branch out into even more ambitious projects than just feeding the neglected of the neighborhood. It was decided that funds would be apportioned to help Russian Jewish immigrants.

Numerous programs were implemented, among them the "Russian Resume Service," in which students wrote up respectable resumes for Russian job-seekers incapable of describing their qualifications in adequate English. An even more enterprising endeavor was

"Friendly Furniture Finders," an effort that was picked up by local and national papers, giving the project an added boost.

The Society advertised that anyone interested in donating their old furniture to needy Russian families had only to phone a specified number and the job was as good as done. As soon as the ad appeared, the boys were swamped with calls. In fact, much of the furniture given away by kindhearted, wealthy families was simply too impractical for the intended recipients. After all, the average Russian immigrant has little need for Renaissance sconces, Victorian wing chairs, early Colonial credenzas, Louis IV candelabras, English Regency tables, Sheraton consoles, Chippendale armoires, George II chaise longues, and Tiffany chandeliers. Accordingly, the Society sold its surfeit to antique shops and used-furniture stores and the proceeds were added to the immigrants' fund.

But of all the Society's activities on behalf of the Russians, the jewel in the crown was the Chanukah party itself. The hundreds who attended were so impressed that it awakened within their hearts a desire to learn about their religion. Most appropriate, and certainly timely, as He Who performed miracles and wonders in those days of old graciously continues to do so in these days as well.

Heard from: Raphael Willig and Danny Wolff

There's Always Room for More

nn Davis was Jewish only by birth, but in her soul a spark waited to be kindled.

Thousands of miles away lived Clara Urdolovich, also Jewish only by birth. But her spark had already been kindled and the fire was richly aglow.

Moscow 1980 had been a world apart from Moscow 1990. Pre-*perestroika* and *glasnost*, Jewish observance of any kind had been strictly forbidden. Indeed, anyone accused of either practicing or promoting Judaism had been persecuted, jailed, and often even exiled.

Remarkably, these threats had not

deterred Clara from engaging in possibly the most dangerous activity of all: conducting a Jewish kindergarten. From the Soviet perspective, this was an unspeakable crime, and teachers like Clara were guilty of nothing less than "poisoning" youngsters' minds and depriving them of their proud communist heritage.

Many Soviet Jewry activists traveled to Russia in the 1980s, smuggling in much-needed religious articles and teaching wherever they could. All were amazed by Clara's bravery and determination. Yet whenever they questioned how she could endanger her own safety so, she would simply reply, "How can I not?" No matter what the risk, Clara did not want Jewish youngsters to be deprived of the religious upbringing that she herself had been denied.

Back in England, amidst freedom and affluence, twenty-year-old Ann Davis began to think about what she could do to help Soviet Jewry. Her thoughts were triggered by her upcoming visit to Russia, a journey that she would be making along with sixteen other undergraduates from the London School of Economics.

Ann had no interest in locating the Jewish underground or teaching anyone Jewish concepts (even if she could have). But she *could* take a parcel with her, thereby doing what she considered her fair share.

With no idea how to go about doing whatever it was she wanted to do, Ann called the JIA (the British equivalent of the United Jewish Appeal) for direction. The JIA gave her the phone number of the National Council for Soviet Jewry. The Council could not think of any way to utilize her services, but since she was so determined to use her trip to benefit others, they advised her (after considerable thought) to try Lubavitch. And she did.

With less than a week until Passover, Lubavitch had already seen to its deliveries. The Lubavitcher who had answered Ann's phone call thanked her for her offer, and was about to tell her to try again next year, when he suddenly had an idea.

"Eddie Hafter," he said, "a businessman in the Golders Green section of London, sends packages to Russia every month. Maybe he has something he would like to send for the holiday."

When Ann reached Eddie Hafter early Friday morning, he was thrilled; he simply couldn't believe the perfect timing of Ann's offer! Just the night before, he had received a call from Clara Urdolovich, requesting provisions for a seder she was to host for thirty-three guests.

Hafter had not wanted to disappoint Clara, but it was already Thursday evening and Pesach was beginning Monday night. Although he had told her he would try, he was certain that it was hopeless. He never dreamed that some college student he had never met before would call up and volunteer to take to Russia anything he wanted to send, regardless of size or weight.

Hafter sped off to a kosher supermarket and spent a small fortune buying groceries for the seder. Only after his station wagon was loaded — and bulging — did Eddie suddenly realize that he had gotten carried away. There was simply no way that any stranger would be willing, or able — or permitted — to carry such an enormous load, even if she were the airline's major stockholder. Nonetheless, he drove to the address he was given and introduced himself.

☙

"Why are you empty-handed?" Ann asked. "Didn't you bring me a parcel?"

Eddie Hafter's heart sank to his feet. He had a station wagon full of Haggados, wine, matzah, horseradish, matzah meal, and other seder essentials, and she wanted to know about a single, solitary *parcel!*

"I... eh... er, I think you'd better come downstairs and see for yourself," Hafter suggested, trying to remain calm.

They walked down to the street together and Eddie pointed to the car. Ann circled the sagging station wagon several times in disbelief. Hafter stood aside, silently praying that Clara would somehow have what she needed to make a seder, that all of his efforts would not be in vain, and that he had not made a total fool of himself in front of this college student.

After several torturously long moments of thought, Ann finally turned to Hafter and declared, "I'll take it all!"

Eddie Hafter resumed breathing.

Ann figured that the students traveling with her would all have very little luggage, and she was confident that she could convince them to share in this good deed with her. Her confidence was not misplaced.

It had never occurred to Hafter that the group would be flying on Shabbos. Indeed, because the flight was on a Saturday and all the students appeared to be gentiles, the Russian customs officials did not even bother to inspect the eleven enormous suitcases containing all the ingredients of Clara's seder.

On Passover eve, Ann and ten burly, luggage-toting classmates met Clara at the appointed site. From there, they shlepped the oversized suitcases up to Clara's tiny apartment.

Ann glanced around the sparsely furnished Urdolovich home and wondered how thirty-three guests would crowd inside. Her thoughts were interrupted by Clara, who seemed to have some urgent matter on her mind.

"And where will *you* be attending the seder this evening?" she asked.

Ann blushed and stammered a bit, and then replied in a whisper that she was not observant. Clara did not appear to understand. Ann tried to explain that she didn't keep kosher or go to synagogue, but her words were incomprehensible to a woman who routinely risked her safety and jeopardized her freedom to observe these very mitzvos.

"It is never too late to start," Clara commented, still obviously confounded by the fact that someone who was free to observe the commandments would not take advantage of the opportunity. "Tonight you will be the thirty-fourth guest at our seder!" she announced with finality. It seemed more like an order than an invitation.

"But... er, I... I, no thank you..." Ann declined, but it soon became clear that she was simply no match for her heroic hostess.

Later that same evening, Ann Davis squeezed her way into the most moving and inspiring event of her lifetime. By the time it was over, the spark within Ann Davis had been kindled.

Heard from: Rabbi Moshe Kupitz

The Judge Knot

There are many reasons for judging others favorably and giving them the benefit of the doubt. First, the Torah commands us to do so. Second, third, and fourth, when one judges others favorably, chances are that he has really judged them correctly. And conversely, one who jumps to conclusions runs the risk of falsely condemning his fellow man. All of this is illustrated in the following story.

The Goldstein home, in the Bayit Vegan neighborhood of Jerusalem, is one where mitzvos are lovingly performed. Naturally, it is a home where strenuous effort is made to engage in *shemiras halashon.* And as we all know, the best way to refrain from *lashon hara* is to give people the benefit of the doubt.

Miriam Tibi is a regular guest at the Goldsteins'. As Miriam comes from a broken home, the Goldsteins make sure she always feels welcome and her presence appreciated. One *erev Shabbos*, however, Miriam showed up wearing a sweater that sixteen-year-old Kaila Goldstein was certain was hers! Granted, it is not uncommon for two people to purchase identical articles of clothing, but this particular sweater was truly one-of-a-kind: a hand-knitted cardigan adorned with rabbit-fur trim.

To her credit, Kaila immediately wished to give Miriam the benefit of the doubt, and assumed that her guest had inadvertently packed the sweater along with her own belongings after a previous visit. However, when she asked Miriam about it, the girl insisted that the sweater was hers.

Miriam's obduracy frustrated not only Kaila but her mother, too, as they both had been looking for that sweater for over a month. Just to be extra sure that they weren't accusing Miriam falsely, they searched through Kaila's closet and dresser drawers yet again — but to no avail.

Friday night after dinner, Kaila discussed the whole matter with her father. Dr. Goldstein was troubled by his daughter's assertion. Not only didn't he feel that there were adequate grounds to accuse Miriam, he feared that the suspicion alone would "poison" the hospitable atmosphere of his home.

"In the absence of solid proof, all you have is 'circumstantial evidence,'" he concluded, dismissing the matter.

On Shabbos morning, however, Kaila remembered that at the back of her sweater there had been a pink, woolen loop sticking out of the weave. She had intended to fix it with a crochet hook but had never gotten around to it. Now that little loop would help her identify the sweater for certain. If a pink loop did indeed stick out at the back of "Miriam's" sweater, then Kaila would have incontrovertible evidence that her guest had actually *taken* her favorite garment.

Ever-so-casually, Kaila walked behind Miriam's seat at the Shabbos table and took a look. Sure enough, the pink loop was there!

Until now, Kaila had pretended to

have forgotten all about the sweater and was behaving just as a gracious hostess should. But now she was unable to resist asking Miriam, "Where did you get this lovely thing?"

"Oh, it was given to me," Miriam replied.

Kaila became even more suspicious. Obviously, Miriam was clever enough not to say she had purchased it somewhere, since no store in the entire Middle East carried such a sweater.

When Shabbos was over, Kaila and her mother thanked Miriam for coming, but they couldn't help feeling that she had taken advantage of her hosts.

Apparently Miriam was not oblivious to the tension in the air because on Sunday night, her mother telephoned Mrs. Goldstein to ask why they thought Miriam had taken Kaila's sweater.

Mrs. Goldstein hesitated for a moment and then said, "Quite frankly, Mrs. Tibi, we feel certain that the cardigan is Kaila's. It was her favorite sweater and it has been missing for over a month. Do you mind telling me where you got it?"

"It was given to us by Rebbetzin Segal," Miriam's mother replied simply.

A very smart answer, Mrs. Goldstein

thought, for Rebbetzin Segal routinely distributed clothing to needy families and there was no way to trace what she gave out.

The sweater affair was still being discussed the next day at breakfast when fourteen-year-old Chanie Goldstein almost swept her bowl of cereal off the table. "Mommy! I just remembered... I accidentally got some ink on Kaila's sweater so I took it to the dry cleaners, but I forgot to pick it up!"

Mrs. Goldstein dashed off to the dry cleaners, hoping against hope that she would indeed be able to retrieve Kaila's sweater, but the cardigan was nowhere to be found.

"When was it given in?" the proprietor asked the distraught mother in response to her inquiry.

"About five weeks ago."

"I'm terribly sorry," he said, "but any garments left here longer than a month without being claimed are given to Rebbetzin Segal. You know, that fine lady who distributes clothing to the poor..."

Heard from: Kaila

A Blood Relation

y the time the Katz baby was eleven days old, he'd been poked, prodded and examined by more doctors than most of us see in a lifetime. Born in the beginning of the seventh month, his very existence was a wonder of Providence and neonatal technology.

The baby had already undergone several hair-raising operations, each one requiring numerous blood transfusions. According to standard hospital procedure, every patient requiring surgery must replace all the units of blood used during his operation, a precaution that insures that hospitals do not deplete their blood supplies

Accordingly, a few days after the infant was born, Rabbi Katz and all his older children dropped by the hospital's blood bank to "make a deposit." As he rolled up his sleeve, Yehoshua Katz (who only a week ago had been the baby of the family) was dismayed to see a sign that read:

> ALL DONORS MUST BE
> AT LEAST SEVENTEEN YEARS OLD.

Yehoshua's seventeenth birthday was three weeks away. The restriction was no more than a technicality, he realized, as he was a robust boy who could easily have passed for twenty-one. He would not be any more robust in three weeks' time.

But Rabbi Katz was not swayed by Yehoshua's rationalization and he forbade his son to donate blood.

"It's not fair!" Yehoshua protested. "I want to help my brother! I won't be hurting anyone, and I won't actually be lying — no one would even think to ask me my age."

From Rabbi Katz's perspective, however, there was no difference. An untruth was also a lie. For the Torah not only prohibits lying, it condemns any form of falsehood.

Angry and hurt, Yehoshua later appealed to his mother to let him donate blood for the baby, but she was well aware of her husband's policy. Rabbi Katz maintained, with solid proof from the Talmud, that there was no way to contain a lie; one violation always led to another.

The next day, almost-seventeen-year-old Yehoshua Katz was involved in a terrible car accident in the Catskill Mountains. He was so severely injured that the HATZOLAH rescue team that pulled him out of the wreckage wasted no time applying tourniquets to his multiple wounds and concentrated their efforts on rushing him to the hospital. Yehoshua had lost so much blood that they feared for his survival.

It turned out that the boy had indeed lost a great deal of blood — over thirty percent! His condition was critical. Five operations and countless feats of microsurgery later, however, Yehoshua was back in one piece, more or less. He had miraculously survived his terrifying ordeal.

"I heard you were trying to donate blood just the day before your accident," one of the surgeons later remarked when Yehoshua was on the road to recovery. "It's a good thing they didn't let you. The body replenishes its complete blood supply after donation, but not that fast. If you had had even one pint less left in you after the crash, well, I doubt you would have made it, kid."

It was then that Yehoshua realized that he owed his life to the value of *emes*, the attribute of truthfulness that his father so zealously upheld.

Heard from: Avraham Mordechai Newman

HONORABLE MENTSCHEN

Light in the Darkness

ot long ago, the entire Soviet Union was one huge prison. Its citizens were deprived of many freedoms we take for granted, including the right to practice our religion and live anywhere we choose, or even to emigrate to another country if we so desire. Any Russian citizen who wanted to leave the Soviet Union was considered a traitor to his country.

Many Russians would have preferred to live elsewhere, *anywhere*, just to be free of oppression, but few were willing to risk being branded disloyal and made to suffer all sorts of demoralizing punishments. One group of Soviet citizens, however, was prepared to take that risk: the Jews. In increasing numbers, the Jews of Russia began to openly declare their desire to leave Mother Russia and resettle in Eretz Yisrael. These fearless Jews were called "prisoners of Zion."

Since the Bolshevik Revolution, hundreds of brave men and women courageous enough to stand up to a ruthless regime became prisoners of Zion. Among them was a young man named Yosef. Remarkably, not only did Yosef proclaim his intention to live in the Land of Israel, he tried to fulfill his dream in a bold, dramatic move that finally made the plight of Russian Jewry known to the whole world.

The day he attempted to escape to Israel in a stolen airplane, he was arrested by the infamous KGB — the Soviet secret police — and condemned to death. Due to pressure applied by free countries all over the world, his sentence was eventually commuted to a long and harsh prison term in Siberia's dreaded Vladimir Prison.

Vladimir was a terrifying institution devoted to the destruction of the human spirit. Inside the prison compound, the living conditions were appalling. Rations varied in caloric content from sub-average to starvation level, exercise and fresh air were minimal and contact with the outside was limited to several letters a year, with this privilege, too, often suspended. Technically, each prisoner was allowed two meetings a year with his family, but years could pass without any visits at all.

The KGB had an elaborate and remarkably pragmatic way of controlling an inmate's body and soul. Once prisoners recovered from the initial shock of life at Vladimir, a KGB representative would invite them in for a talk. They would be offered coffee, tea, meat, or a visit to a restaurant in civilian clothing. An officer from the secret police might even tempt them with a letter from their family, or a visit with a friend.

To earn these privileges, a prisoner merely had to be willing to inform on a cellmate, or confess to a crime he never committed. Naturally, Yosef refused to do either, so he was denied all religious articles, as well as permission to perform mitzvos. But for all its unspeakable terror, intimidation, demoralization, and frequent punishments, the KGB couldn't break Yosef's iron will to fulfill God's commandments.

Somehow he managed to observe, in the most primitive fashion imaginable, whatever mitzvos he could. He virtually risked his life by not working on Shabbos. He refused to eat non-kosher food and avoided *chametz* on Passover. He made a *tallis* for himself, always kept his head covered, and even performed the mitzvah of searching for *chametz*.

One frigid winter, a single thought managed to warm Yosef's soul: Chanukah was approaching. Commemorating the victory of the pure and the weak over the evil and powerful, Chanukah celebrates the triumph of right over might, the triumph of the spirit over the forces of terror.

Yosef dreamed of lighting a Chanukah menorah, a virtual impossibility under the circumstances. Certainly the prison authorities would never permit the performance of this mitzvah and would react harshly to the very notion. Regardless, Yosef put his mind to the mission and developed a clever, viable scheme.

Every day he saved a little of his

meager rations, even though this meant subsisting on a starvation diet. When no one was watching, he secretly slipped a crust of bread or a sliver of potato into his pocket. Later on, he carefully stashed these precious scraps on a small ledge in his cell, and prayed that no guard would notice his curious cache. Hoarding food was considered a criminal act, and if discovered, not only would the food be confiscated, but the perpetrator would suffer a cruel punishment as well. As with every other mitzvah he performed in Vladimir Prison, Yosef accepted the risk.

The day before Chanukah, Yosef could scarcely contain his excitement. So far his little collection had gone unnoticed. Now there was only one final, critical detail to be arranged. Trying to attract as little attention as possible, Yosef traded some of his rations to another prisoner for a pack of cigarettes and a box of matches. He had no use for the cigarettes, but the matches were the crucial missing ingredient for his plan.

Fingers trembling, Yosef opened the box of matches and found forty-four matches inside, exactly the number he needed, to serve as the Chanukah lights.

And so, late on the first night of

Chanukah, when everyone was finally asleep and no guards were in sight, Yosef inserted the matches into his scraps of bread and potato and fashioned a secret Chanukah menorah! The matches burned for only a few seconds, but they provided endless light and inspiration for Yosef Mendelevich in the depths of the Vladimir Prison in Siberia.

Heard from: Yacov Mordechai

Food for Thought

Shmuel (Shorty) Abramowitz punched a new hole in his belt and then pulled it tightly around his waist. The long end drooped down his leg like an anteater's tongue and his trousers ballooned around his hips. "Looks like I've lost a little weight," he joked, but the truth was that he'd lost a *lot* of weight, more than a person of his size could afford to part with and still remain healthy.

"It doesn't matter," he thought to himself. "Soon I'll be back in Mom's kitchen and she'll fatten me up for sure!"

Yes, Shorty's tour of duty in the United States Army was almost over and in just a few weeks, he'd be shipped home. His mouth watered and his head swam as he remembered the Shabbos and Yom Tov meals in his parents' home.

But now was no time for reminiscing. It was his first day on this army post and he didn't want to be late for mess call. In the army, everyone had to adhere to a strict schedule.

Nervously, Corporal Abramowitz stood in line with the other soldiers, but unlike most of them, he did not extend his metal bowl. The mess sergeant was doling out portions of strange-smelling food and each soldier enthusiastically accepted his share, but Shorty only scanned the length of the serving table, searching for something edible — that is, something kosher. He found nothing.

The mess sergeant was a burly Irishman who was rumored to be the army's heavyweight boxing champion. Shorty tried to avoid eye contact with him as he passed by, his plate still empty. Twice his height and at least triple his weight, Sergeant McElroy looked as if he could eat Shorty for breakfast and still be hungry. When he saw that the little corporal had refused to take any food, McElroy turned purple with rage.

With his arms folded aggressively across his massive chest, McElroy boomed, "Hey, you — Midget! — don't you want any lunch?"

Shorty winced and pretended not to have heard. As casually as possible, he scooped some peas and rice onto his plate and prepared to make a quick get-away. But McElroy stepped out from behind the serving table and grabbed him by his shirt front.

"What's the matter, Pint-Size, don't you like my cooking?" he demanded.

Shorty's mind raced. Three times a day for the next few weeks, he would be under McElroy's watchful eye. Even if he managed to survive this first meeting, there was no guarantee that he'd survive the next. If he were to tell the giant that he simply wasn't hungry now, what excuse could he give at suppertime? And if he said that he had a sensitive stomach, McElroy might seek to "desensitize" it with a swift right hook.

Despite the imposing muscle-man towering over him, Shorty decided to do the riskiest thing of all: to tell the truth. "I am a religious Jew," he whispered meekly, "and I may only eat kosher food. When I was drafted, I promised my mother that I would not compromise my religious principles. Thank God, until now I have kept that promise."

As these words passed his lips, Shorty felt himself growing inside. In his youth he'd suffered countless beatings at the hands of schoolyard bullies. Now, for the first time in his life, he'd actually stood up to one, and for once he felt strong enough to take whatever was coming.

Suddenly McElroy's face turned even purpler and his eyes began to water. "I also promised my mother something," he confessed, his voice choked with emotion, "but I... I..." The giant covered his face with his hands and wept like a baby. "I'm just not as tough as you are," he sobbed. "I broke my promise."

Shorty was so touched that he reached out to pat McElroy on the shoulder, but his hand only came to the sergeant's elbow. "There, there," he said gently. "Your mom will understand."

Realizing that everyone was staring at him, the mess sergeant quickly wiped away his tears.

"Come with me," he ordered sternly, and Abramowitz obediently followed McElroy into the kitchen. Once inside, the sergeant made a sweeping gesture with his hand, taking in all the vegetables, fruits, canned goods, preserves, dairy products, and other assorted foodstuffs cramming the shelves. "You can come back here whenever you want," he told Shorty, "and take anything you're allowed to eat. And if anyone gives you a hard time, just tell 'em Slugger sent you."

Heard from: Yaakov Feldheim

The Bricklayer of Buchenwald

We will never understand how it was possible to survive even one day in the Buchenwald concentration camp. Camp survivors will never understand how Reb Eliezer Zadok lived there for five-and-a-half years.

Life in Buchenwald could hardly be called "living." The Nazis did everything possible to see to that. Not only were inmates cut off from their relatives and friends, stripped of their possessions, and denied proper nourishment, they were robbed of their pride and dignity, subjected to backbreaking labor, constant humiliation, and savage beatings around the clock.

There was only one way for the defenseless prisoners to fight back: by somehow remaining human under those inhuman circumstances. Their only ammunition was their faith, and in this regard, Reb Eliezer Zadok was well armed.

As miraculous and wondrous as it sounds, Eliezer Zadok — then just twenty-seven years old, and an orphan to boot — arranged fifteen minutes of "time-off" on Yom Kippur for prayer, and distributed matzos — baked on the premises — during Pesach. Furthermore, he organized a daily *minyan* in Buchenwald during roll call. As the Nazis counted out how many Jews had managed to survive one more demonic day of unspeakable torture, Eliezer and company affirmed that there is only one God and one Judge, and to Him alone is man accountable.

As if such an astounding achievement weren't proof enough of what an incredible person Reb Eliezer was, friends and fellow survivors are quick to confirm that this was not even his greatest accomplishment. They point to his endless acts of kindness on behalf of his fellow prisoners in the camp, and to how, after the war was finally over, he remained behind on Europe's blood-soaked soil to care for dozens of Jewish orphans who craved spiritual direction and affection. Without his loving care, it is unlikely that those homeless children would ever have survived as practicing or even believing Jews.

But perhaps the most astonishing story about Reb Eliezer surfaced a few days after he returned his holy soul to his Maker. As his wife and sons were sitting *shivah* in the Washington Heights neighborhood of New York, a very distinguished-looking stranger came to comfort the family.

Introducing himself as Rabbi Friedman, a *rosh kollel* in Williamsburg, he claimed that he owed his life to Reb Eliezer Zadok.

"I arrived at Buchenwald towards the end of the war," he began. "A skinny teenager much younger than your father, my chances of survival were slim — until I met him. He explained that a Jew in Buchenwald was allowed to live only as long as he served the needs of the Third Reich. Once he was no longer needed, or was physically unable to continue his slave labor, the Nazis dispensed with him.

"As a bricklayer," Rabbi Friedman continued, "your father possessed a vital skill. Although I knew nothing about masonry, he instructed me to pretend to be his assistant. My job was only to haul the mortar and mix it, but Reb Eliezer insisted that this required some professional talent that only I possessed. In this way, he convinced the Germans that I was an asset — that is, someone worth keeping alive.

"One day — it came out in the course of conversation — your father learned that I was a *kohen.* All of a sudden, the same man who had been starved, beaten, and victimized for over five years in Buchenwald looked as if he'd just suffered his greatest punishment. He grabbed my arm, looked into my eyes, and declared: 'You will not shlep anything more for me!'

"He was referring, of course, to the law in *Shulchan Aruch* prohibiting a *Yisrael* from having a *kohen* work for him — a law rarely observed even during peacetime!

"Sure enough, until the day of our liberation, in order to comply with halachah your father forbade me to do any work for him, thereby doubling his own workload!"

In his matchless modesty, Reb Eliezer Zadok had never seen fit to share this story, like so many others, with his family. Fortunately, Rabbi Friedman did.

Heard from: Uri Davidson

Stranded Simchah

ivkie and Shmuel Jacobs were married in Brooklyn and their first *sheva brachos* was hosted by the *kallah*'s family. For Shabbos the newlyweds were invited to Lakewood, New Jersey, where their second, third, and fourth *sheva brachos* were to take place. A friend of Shmuel's offered to drive them.

On Friday morning, as they were preparing for their two-hour trip, they learned that Shmuel's father had no means of getting to Lakewood. Rivkie and Shmuel felt terrible. They had been so caught up in the whirlwind of excitement surrounding their wedding that they hadn't thought about Mr. Jacobs' travel arrangements.

"Please, Abba," Shmuel offered, "You can ride with my friend. We'll take the bus."

And that is precisely what they did.

This trip, however, was not destined to be uneventful. From the moment the bus departed from the Port Authority terminal in New York City until it merged onto the highway to Lakewood one-and-a-half hours later, it was snarled in traffic.

Shabbos was quickly approaching, but Rivkie and Shmuel weren't quickly approaching Lakewood. Unless the traffic miraculously cleared up and the bus traveled at top speed, not only would they never make it to their *sheva brachos*, but they would be stranded somewhere on the highway for Shabbos. The thought was as chilling as the weather, which had turned bitter cold. To make matters worse, rain began to fall in a steady downpour.

Twenty minutes before candlelighting time, Shmuel and Rivkie got off the bus in Freehold, New Jersey, and tried their luck at hailing a cab. When this plan failed, they resigned themselves to the only option available.

Fighting the wind and rain, they set off on foot in the direction of the Badelia Yeshivah, which Shmuel remembered was within walking distance of Freehold. One teacher in the yeshivah was the noted Rabbi Dovid Lieberman, who, together with his wife, was known never to pass up an opportunity to perform a mitzvah, regardless of the hardship involved.

The hope of reaching the Lieberman home was what kept Rivkie and Shmuel trudging through the frigid, pouring rain. No matter how far they veered from the side of the road, however, every passing vehicle managed to drench them afresh with giant, angry waves as it sped by.

Somehow Rivkie and Shmuel found their way to the Liebermans' and anxiously rapped on the front door. Between the thunder outside and the spirited *niggunim* coming from the Shabbos table inside, they had to knock loudly.

When Rabbi and Mrs. Lieberman opened their door at last, they discovered a soaking young couple shivering on their doorstep. Without waiting for an introduction, they greeted the weary

strangers with a hearty "Come in, come in! *Gutt Shabbos!*" Mrs. Lieberman ran to fetch dry clothing while Rabbi Lieberman handed out towels.

When Rivkie and Shmuel had warmed up a bit, they related how they had ushered in the first Shabbos of their married lives trekking through a downpour on the highway. They'd been wed only two nights ago, they explained, and now they had missed their *sheva brachos* in Lakewood.

"You didn't miss a thing," Rabbi Lieberman assured them with a twinkle in his eye. "Come to the table and make kiddush, and I'll be back in just a little while." Before they knew what was happening, the rabbi had grabbed his overcoat and was out the door.

True to his word, Rabbi Lieberman returned a few minutes later, but he wasn't alone. Some forty students from the yeshivah accompanied him, and they were only too eager, after Rabbi Lieberman's gentle encouragement, to continue their Shabbos meal at their teacher's home.

Rabbi Lieberman understood just how frustrated Rivkie and Shmuel were by the day's events. Without realizing it, they had come to the right address. They would yet have a *sheva brachos* that they would cherish for the rest of their lives.

Indeed, the gusto and fervor of the students' dancing and singing were so joyous, it was as if they were attending an actual wedding! The Jacobses quickly forgot their misfortune, and everyone present was delighted to participate in the special mitzvah of rejoicing with a bride and groom.

Heard from: Elimelech Trenk

To Save a Life

There is never any excuse for leaving dangerous objects within reach. This lesson was painfully re-learned many years ago in Camp Agudah when a hapless camper tripped over a broken broom handle that was left on the ground. The broom handle punctured his skin and part of it remained imbedded in his thigh. Little Davey Shwartz was rushed to the infirmary but he required more extensive medical treatment than the camp could provide.

Shimon Yitzchak (Shimmy) Askovitz, a counselor who was "off-duty" that Thursday morning, volunteered to drive Davey to a hospital nearby. The camper was quickly admitted to the emergency room, where a doctor and nurse gently washed the wound, removed all of the splinters that had pierced Davey's skin, and sent the young patient back to camp.

But Davey's ordeal was far from over. All night long he was in agony and the next morning there was no improvement. By Friday afternoon, the boy was in such bad shape that Shimmy rushed him back to the hospital. The signs of infection were unmistakable: Davey's thigh was swollen and purple and he had a raging fever. The doctors tried various methods of lowering his temperature, but all to no avail.

Had this episode occurred in 1991, or even 1951, the treatment would have been routine. But it was 1941, a few years before the antibiotics we take for granted today were available. With nothing to combat the spread of infection, patients often died of ailments as common as strep throat. Consequently, the doctors in the hospital feared that Davey's condition was hopeless, and they promptly gave up on him.

Fortunately, third-year medical student Shimon Yitzchak Askovitz did not.

Shimmy had encountered this feeling of helplessness far too often in his young life. In fact, it was the reason he had gone into medicine in the first place. He couldn't bear to stand idly by while a child lay dying.

Suddenly, Shimmy recalled something he had heard months earlier at a lecture in medical school. One of his professors had mentioned the discovery of a revolutionary drug called "penicillin," which had proven successful in combating infection. So far, its use had been restricted to soldiers fighting in World War II, but further research was under way at his medical school.

Seconds later, Shimmy was fulfilling the Torah's commandment to desecrate Shabbos in order to save a life. As fast as he could, he drove to the University of Pennsylvania Medical School in Philadelphia, to try and locate the new wonder drug.

In record time, Shimmy accomplished his mission. With two vials of penicillin in hand, he raced back to the hospital in upstate New York, but when he presented the precious life-saving medicine to the hospital staff, no one was willing to administer it. They were afraid to take responsibility for a medication they had never heard of. If the boy were to die as a result, they would be blamed.

Shimmy was more afraid of what might happen if Davey did *not* get the medicine. So, with a prayer on his lips, he personally administered the penicillin and then kept a round-the-clock vigil at his patient's bedside.

By Tuesday morning, there was a marked improvement. It appeared that the boy would live. That evening, Davey's fever broke and he was conscious and alert. To celebrate the moment, Shimmy recited *havdallah* for his patient and himself, and then ate his first morsel of food in three days.*

This was the first time that Dr. Simon I. Askovitz had saved a life, but it certainly was not the last. This was but the beginning of a life-time career of healing, helping, and caring for others, each case marked by the same disregard for his own well-being, the same concern for his patient, and the same prayer on his lips: "May Hashem guide my hands..."

Heard from: Dr. Eli Eilenberg

Halachah mandates that one may not partake of food after Shabbos until hearing the *havdallah* service.

The Singing Soldier

Go to the Kosel any night of the week. There you will find Reb Shmuel fervently pouring out his heart to the Almighty. He is very easy to identify because his voice is so beautiful that it grabs your attention and doesn't let go. His every prayer is obviously a jewel that he treasures dearly; each word is sung in a unique melody that bounces off the stones of the Kosel and echoes like the chime of a great, bronze bell.

The uninitiated might mistake Reb Shmuel for some kind of official "*Kosel chazzan*," someone paid to lead the prayers at the Western Wall every evening. But that is not the case. Reb Shmuel prays at the Wall so faithfully only because of what happened the very *first* time he went there.

&

It was June 7, 1967, right in the middle of the Six-Day War. Reb Shmuel was a member of the paratroop strike force that spearheaded the liberation of Jerusalem's Old City.

Not especially strong or fit, Reb Shmuel was also twenty years older than most of the soldiers in his unit, and already a grandfather. But then, Reb Shmuel wasn't selected for this crack commando brigade because of his combat experience or military know-how.

He was assigned to his unit just a few days before the war began, when he, like most Israeli men age fifty-five or younger, had been "called up" to the reserves. Whenever Israel sees a crisis looming, it calls up its reserve soldiers to increase the size of its army. Reb Shmuel routinely fulfills his military duty as a chaplain.

As a chaplain in the Israel Defense

Forces, one of Reb Shmuel's primary responsibilities was to tend to the critically wounded and make sure that no bodies were abandoned on the battlefield. (Years later, during the Yom Kippur War, Reb Shmuel bravely dragged soldier after soldier out of burning tanks, an act of heroism that earned him a medal from the Chief of Staff.)

On the third morning of the Six-Day War, the command was issued to capture the Old City. The Lions' Gate was selected as the penetration point and Reb Shmuel's platoon of paratroopers, supported by a small armored unit, began the assault. They were met by fierce return-fire, which they soon silenced, but the battle was not yet over. Dozens of well-hidden snipers had staked out the other entrances and alleys of the Old City. Because the Israeli troops had to advance rapidly to get themselves out of sniper range, they raced across the sacred ground of the Temple Mount itself.

Reb Shmuel has never quite forgiven himself for this unintentional desecration of the holiest of all soil. (One may not set foot on the Temple Mount without being ritually pure, an impossibility until the arrival of the Mashiach.) Accordingly, he returns to the Kosel every single night of the year to beg forgiveness, as it were, for defiling the sacred site he had been privileged to liberate.

Heard from: Rabbi Binyamin Glickman

The Mitzvah Maven

Clara and Chaim Baum considered themselves lucky: lucky to be living in Israel (Clara is a Russian immigrant); lucky to have found each other late in life (they are both in their early forties); and lucky to be blessed with a child.

A few days after their daughter was born, however, the Baums learned that she had a rare heart defect and needed an operation immediately. Their doctor explained that the best heart specialists for this complicated surgery were in America, and he urged the Baums to explore the possibility of traveling abroad.

Clara and Chaim didn't know what

there was to explore. They were ready to do anything to save their baby's life and set off for the El Al ticket office without a second thought. Inexperienced travelers that they were, however, they neglected to see to the preparations necessary before purchasing a ticket.

The clerk behind the counter booked their reservation and then began to run through the standard questions:

"How will you be paying for your tickets?"

"We don't know just yet."

"Where are your visas?"

"Visas?" the couple repeated blankly.

"The documents," explained a helpful gentleman waiting behind them on line, "permitting non-Americans to visit America. They are issued after you have been interviewed at the American embassy and have filed a visa application."

Gamely, the clerk continued her routine inquiries:

"Do you have special medical permission to fly with a baby just a few days old?"

"Of course," Chaim replied, relieved that there was at least one question he could answer. "Our doctor said the baby must be operated upon immediately."

"Do you have this in writing?"

It looked like the Baums' luck had run out. With each question, their faces fell lower; they simply had no idea how to proceed.

The ground hostess obviously could not issue the tickets but, seeing how miserable the Baums were, she referred them to Miriam, her superior. As El Al's resident genius at problem-solving, she has a talent for working minor "miracles." In fact, in certain circles, Miriam is known as a "mitzvah maven."

Miriam listened sympathetically to the Baums' predicament and realized immediately that they would never manage on their own. Although *they* had no answers to her questions, she *did* — and the right ones at that. It was as if the Baums' unusual and grave problem were one that she faced routinely. There was no need to explain the urgency of the situation to Miriam, for not only is she a mother herself, she devotes her life to helping others. The Baums' luck had not run out after all.

Before their astonished eyes, Miriam moved into high gear, pressing buttons, dictating a fax, and calling in favors all over the world. The Baums had no idea what was going on, but in seconds Miriam motioned for them to follow her outside. She helped them into her car and drove them to the American embassy, where she used her influence to secure on-the-spot visas.

Next, she phoned the Bostoner Rebbe in Boston, Massachusetts to clear the way for an operation in Boston Children's Hospital. Then she acquired the necessary medical authorization and even borrowed the money to finance the trip from *Keren Avichai,* a private family charity.

Within an hour, the Baums were on their way and Miriam was back at her desk, assisting other travelers, solving problems, and working minor "miracles" — with a little help from Above.

Heard from: Nachman Klieman

ONE GOOD TURN

One Mitzvah Leads to Another

ordechai Amster washed up on the shores of America at the conclusion of World War II. An orphan without relatives or friends in the United States, Mordechai soon found a home in Brooklyn's Torah Vodaas Yeshivah. The administration of the yeshivah, noting his fine character and keen sense of responsibility, promptly appointed him dormitory counselor.

Mordechai became very popular among the students when he opened a "canteen" — a snack bar selling various food items — on the yeshivah premises. Rather than squandering his profits on potato chips, soda, and licorice, he saved up for a real treat: a visit to Eretz Yisrael.

By 1964, the year of the fifth *Knessiah Gedolah* (a convention of great Torah authorities, held in Jerusalem), Mordechai had amassed enough pennies, nickels, and dimes to afford the trip.

In those days, most people sailed to Israel; very few aside from businessmen flew. But Mordechai had made a reservation aboard a non-nonstop propellor flight. Because of the uniqueness of this mode of travel, every passenger drove to the airport in a car full of relatives bearing bags filled with cookies, cakes, fruit, and other snacks to tide him over on the long journey.

When Mordechai saw all the families fussing over their Israel-bound relatives, he couldn't help but feel lonely. There was no one there to see him off.

Back in Brooklyn, however, a Torah Vodaas student thought to himself, "Our dorm counselor is flying to Israel and no one even went with him to the airport!" A moment later, Hirsh Goldberg was out on the street hailing a taxi.

Since this was before the days of terrorists and tight security, Hirsh was able to walk right up to the boarding gate

and catch Mordechai just as he was about to leave the terminal. "Mordy! Mordy!" Hirsh cried out, and Mordechai stopped in his tracks to see who was calling him. As soon as he saw Hirsh running towards him, his heart filled with joy. The two friends embraced and their tears mingled.

Hirsh Goldberg had been a true friend and Mordechai Amster never forgot it.

Not long after Mordechai returned from Israel, Hirsh became engaged. The wedding was to take place the following year but something happened in the middle. Hirsh suddenly became very ill and rumors spread that his engagement had been called off. With each passing month, Hirsh's condition deteriorated and eventually he was hospitalized.

Everyone in Torah Vodaas was shocked to learn that Hirsh Goldberg had contracted multiple sclerosis (MS), an incurable disease of the nervous system. Although Hirsh was now bedridden, his mind remained as sharp and clear as ever. This was the hardest part of the disease for Hirsh to bear. A diligent student, he had always loved attending classes in yeshivah. Once he was hospitalized, it was as if his lifeline had been cut.

One day, Mordechai Amster, eager to repay Hirsh for his thoughtful gesture at the airport, had an idea. With the cassette industry just beginning to develop, Mordechai became one of its earliest supporters. First he purchased two tape recorders and dozens of blank cassettes. Then he enlisted distinguished scholars to record their classes.

The cassettes were the greatest gift Hirsh could have received. Not only did they give him a new lease on life, they also guaranteed him constant company, for his fellow Jewish patients flocked to his bedside to share in his learning.

Meanwhile Mordechai kept upgrading his recording equipment, but Hirsh and the other patients in the hospital were not the only ones to profit from this instance of one mitzvah causing another. It was in Hirsh's humble hospital room that "Torah Tapes" was born, a project from which so many of us continue to benefit. And to this very day, it is "Mordechai Amster" who runs the American end of the operation.

Heard from: Rabbis Yoel Burstyn and Meir Applebaum

Paid in Full

I t is not surprising that the holiest city in the world is also the most memorable place to celebrate a Yom Tov. And anyone who has had the privilege of being in Jerusalem for the holidays can tell you that Sukkos is the most special Yom Tov of all.

The week before the festival, the entire city seems to reverberate with the clang of hammers driving nails into sukkah walls. The streets of Jerusalem's religious neighborhoods swarm with countless merchants selling *arba'ah minim*, sukkah construction materials, and colorful decorations. The roadways are clogged with vehicles hauling *s'chach*, and so many people seek the halachic "seal of approval" for their *esrogim* and *lulavim* that the lines outside *poskim*'s houses stretch around the block.

And all this before the holiday even *begins*!

Once Sukkos actually arrives, everyone dons his Yom Tov finery, and men and boys parade around every inch of the city with the most varied and unusual *lulav* carrying cases and *esrog* boxes. On the home front it is commonplace for a family singing a *zemer* in their sukkah to be joined by neighbors harmonizing in *their* sukkah, and then the voices of *their* neighbors chime in, until an entire neighborhood is merrily singing the very same tune!

But by far the highlight of Sukkos in Jerusalem is the *simchas beis hashoevah* phenomenon. Every night at various yeshivos and synagogues, there is lively music, dancing, and singing until the small hours of the morning. No matter where you are in Jerusalem during *chol hamoed Sukkos*, as soon as night falls, drums start beating and clarinets pierce the air. One who has seen Jerusalem celebrate for an entire week has little trouble understanding why the festival is known as *zeman simchaseinu*.

That's why Bert Lerner, a wealthy American businessman who visits Israel every Sukkos just to get recharged by all the joy, was so surprised to see the white-bearded man standing next to him at the Slonimer *simchas beis hashoevah* look so glum.

"What's the matter?" he asked. "Are you feeling all right?"

Feivel Rabinowitz looked at the gentleman who had posed the question, sized him up, and then replied, "I've got a problem. I live in B'nei Brak but I came to visit the Rebbe for the holiday. Of course, the Rebbe gave me a blessing, but he issued me an order as well. You see, I am a fundraiser for the Slonimer institutions," Rabinowitz explained, "and we are so short of funds that our teachers have not been paid for over three months. The Rebbe has therefore forbidden me to leave Jerusalem until I raise $20,000!"

"That shouldn't be too difficult for an experienced fundraiser," Bert remarked. "Surely there are plenty of people willing to give to a worthy cause at this time of year."

"Normally that would be true," Feivel conceded, "but I have already approached

anyone and everyone I know in Jerusalem so many times in the past that I am simply embarrassed to go back to them. Now I don't know where to turn."

Bert considered Rabinowitz's predicament and pondered it over for a minute or two. "I'll make you a deal," he offered. "My name is Lerner and I'm staying at the Plaza Hotel. If you can raise $10,000 by Monday evening, I'll match it!"

Rabinowitz's eyes lit up. He grabbed the American businessman's hand, shook it warmly, and then rushed into the circle of dancers, kicking every which way and flailing his arms as though he were the happiest man in the world.

At 6:25 P.M. the following Monday, Feivel Rabinowitz arrived at the Plaza looking for Lerner. Bert invited the fundraiser up to his room, whereupon Rabinowitz proudly displayed his accomplishment: $10,000 in travelers' checks, bank drafts, personal checks, and cash in several currencies. The two men totaled everything up and then, true to his word, Bert took out his checkbook

and wrote the Slonimer Yeshivah a check for $10,000.

As Rabinowitz stared at the check, his eyes began to swim. In a trembling voice, he whispered, "Why... I don't even know you! Why have you been so generous toward me?"

Bert sighed and seemed to drift off in a nostalgic reverie. "But I *do* know you," he said at last. "And I'm not being generous, either — I'm merely repaying a long-overdue debt."

Lerner sat his elderly guest down in an armchair and began to tell his story:

"Thirty years ago, I was a poor boy. So poor that I didn't even have enough money to buy a new hat for my wedding. On the day of my *chassunah*, I shuffled down Division Avenue in Williamsburg, bemoaning the fact that the shabby clothing I was wearing was exactly what I would wear to my *chuppah*. Finally, mustering all my courage, I walked into a hat store and explained my predicament to the proprietor. I pleaded with him to give me a hat, assuring him that I would pay for it right after the wedding, using the money my *kallah* and I expected to receive in wedding presents.

"For whatever reason, he decided to

trust me. But that was not all. He told me he was willing to charge me only half price, but he wanted his neighbor down the block to do his share as well.

"I followed his lead and entered the liquor store he had pointed out. The storekeeper listened to my story and gave me a few bottles of schnapps — also at half price — in exchange for my promise to pay him back as soon as I had the money.

"As I walked out of the store, I felt like a new man. Now I would surely have a dignified wedding: I would be a properly dressed groom, and my guests would be able to make a respectable '*l'chaim.*'

"Just then, I looked up and saw *you* crossing the street. Like every other kid in Williamsburg, I knew you were the liveliest *chassunah* dancer in all of Brooklyn.

"With my newfound confidence, I approached you with the same proposition I had made to the hatter and the liquor store owner. I implored you to enliven what would otherwise be a very plain and humble wedding. You weren't sure you could make it, but you took down the details.

"Then that night, in the middle of the

wedding, you burst into the hall and electrified the crowd. You danced as only you know how, helping to make my wedding the most special day of my life.

"Naturally, I paid back the hatter and the liquor store owner, but I never did get around to paying you back... until tonight."

Based on a story heard from: Rabbis Yiddel Ackerman and Paysach Krohn

Credit Where Credit is Due

The Ner Israel Rabbinical College boasts students from yeshivah high schools all over America, but only one pupil from St. Michael's Academy in Brattleboro, Vermont. What's more, Father Peter Cummings, the Academy's librarian, was the one who sent him there!

Although Jonathan Silver never dreamed he would end up in a yeshivah, he always knew he was Jewish. He attended St. Michael's only because academically it was the best high school in the area. (Clearly, his parents were not particularly concerned about their child's Jewish education.)

Jonathan was a good student, but

when it came time to graduate, he was short one course credit. The dean of St. Michael's offered to waive the credit requirement if Jonathan would write a paper about a famous religious leader.

Like any senior, Jonathan was eager to do whatever was necessary to finish high school. So he approached the school library with a bold project in mind: he would write about one of the most celebrated religious figures of all — none other than Rabbi Akiva.

Jonathan's dean had obviously had other personalities in mind when he had thought up the assignment, but no one could deny that Rabbi Akiva met the requirements.

Quite understandably, the St. Michael's library was not exactly well-stocked with background material about the life and times of Rabbi Akiva, so Jonathan turned to the librarian, Father Cummings, for assistance.

The cleric's curiosity was aroused. Why had the student chosen this subject? he wondered.

Jonathan confided to him that he was Jewish and Rabbi Akiva was therefore a more meaningful religious personality to him than any Christian figure might be.

Father Cummings listened carefully, thought for a moment, and then said, "You've got it all wrong, my boy. You shouldn't be writing about Rabbi Akiva, you should be *studying* him!" And with that, he pulled open his desk drawer and removed a *Mishnayos* and a *Chumash*. For the rest of the school year, the librarian devoted an hour a day to teaching Jonathan Silver about his own religion.

Jonathan couldn't help but wonder how Father Cummings knew so much about Judaism and why he was so willing to share his knowledge with the solitary Jewish student at St. Michael's. The librarian simply explained that it was his way of repaying a debt.

Several years earlier, as a young divinity student preparing for ordination, Father Cummings had visited the Holy Land. At the Western Wall, he was "picked up" by Rabbi Meir Schuster, who spends the better part of his days and nights befriending tourists at the Kosel and other sites frequented by college-age youth so that he can invite them to attend classes on Judaism. Rabbi Schuster had assumed that the young man was

Jewish, and Cummings did nothing to convince him otherwise.

Without any coercion whatsoever, Rabbi Schuster had encouraged Peter Cummings to enroll at Ohr Somayach, a Jerusalem yeshivah catering to assimilated Jews who wish to explore their Jewish roots.

Cummings spent over half a year at Ohr Somayach, studying seriously and revealing his secret to no one. He acquired so much knowledge during that period that he felt he owed a debt of gratitude to the Jewish People. By steering Jonathan Silver in the proper direction, he hoped he had at last repaid his debt.

Heard from: Rabbi Yosef Tendler and Dov Wolowitz

EAST SIDE STORIES

A Stitch in Time

The explosion at the door threw Sam Wikler's heart into tachycardia, and each contraction forced the blood through his head with ever-increasing pressure. He had barely recovered from the first attack when the door exploded again. It was 7:15 Sunday morning, a solid hour before any earthling west of the Greenwich Meridian was supposed to stir, and at least three hours before the performance of the Gotham rituals of hauling in the Sunday paper and washing the car. Regardless, someone was banging down Sam Wikler's door *at 7:15 on a Sunday morning!*

Sam forced his eyes open, climbed

into a robe and shuffled to the door. There, he found that the person causing all the havoc was none other than little but not petite Mrs. Maria Munisteri, the wife of his childhood friend Anthony.

"Eh, er, come in, Mrs. Munisteri. It's good to see you so *early* in the morning."

Sam's guest, whose complexion was as sallow as parchment, with rings under her eyes like obsidian blisters, responded by dabbing at her tears with an enormous, soiled handkerchief.

"How's Tony?" Wikler asked innocently.

"We needa help!" Maria half said, half sobbed.

That much Wikler had already gathered.

"You tinka you help?" she addressed him in Italian-Lower East Side Creole, a dialect with more vowels than consonants — which often cropped up in the oddest places — and more nouns than verbs.

Someone else might have grudgingly responded, "Do I have a choice?" but not Samuel J. Wikler, Esq., Attorney at Law. He viewed helping out friends and neighbors as nothing less than his sacred privilege and solemn duty. In Sam's book, the institution of friendship was as thick as blood; there was virtually nothing he wouldn't do for an old pal. But this credo was soon to be put to the ultimate test.

"I can certainly try to help," he offered, attempting to console his distraught visitor.

"But it's a vera bigga favor..."

Sam caught her drift, but she had nothing to fear. He would never charge Tony his regular legal fee.

"Don't worry about the price, Mrs. Munisteri," he assured her magnanimously. "You know Tony and I go back a long way."

"I notta worry bouta that."

Then what could she be worried about? Sam wondered, waiting for Maria to gulp back her tears and regain control of herself.

"Tony, mya Tony, he'sa got bigga trouble."

"Oh, you needn't be overly concerned. I've handled serious criminal problems before. As a matter of fact, I've never lost a case yet. I'm sure it's his first offense so there's really nothing..."

Sam droned on and on, trying to put

Maria at ease, but for all his grandiloquence, the woman appeared no less agitated.

"Tony, he'sa in trouble," she finally blurted out, "but notta with the Law."

Sam Wikler blinked in astonished silence. How could someone get "in trouble" with anything but the Law? He decided to start again.

"Maria, if it's money you need, I'll gladly lend it to you. How many times did Tony stake me when I was short a nickel or a dime for an egg cream or a double feature at Loew's?"

Mrs. Munisteri continued to shake her head, indicating that Wikler hadn't understood a thing. "No, no, it'sa notta money trouble, it'sa *molti* bigga trouble."

"Is he in jail?" Sam asked in a hushed tone.

"Ay, if he was only ina jail..." she moaned, casting her eyes heavenward as though envisioning a dream come true.

Wikler's legally honed mind was all tied up in knots. Thoroughly exasperated, he demanded, "Mrs. Munisteri, is this a civil or a criminal suit?"

"*Exactimenti!*" she proclaimed, as if a career dunce had just related his first intelligent statement.

"Exactly?!"

"Like-a you say. It's a criminal suit!" With great flourish, she proceeded to pull a newly tailored suit out of a paper shopping bag for Sam's inspection.

"Very nice," Sam said, admiring what was clearly Tony's handiwork. The material was obviously imported and the stitching and detail were more masterful than any he had ever beheld. The coat and trousers were nothing short of a work of art, and the waistcoat boasted scarlet, silk lining, tastefully pointed lapels, and... and an enormous gash cutting all the way up through the lower right watch pocket.

"Yikes!" Sam yelped. "Fixing this looks like a challenge that even a master tailor like Tony would be hard-pressed to handle."

"That'sa the whole problem!" Maria exclaimed, breaking into a fresh bout of crying.

Now that the "whole problem" had been explained to him, Sam Wikler still had no idea what it was. In fact, he hadn't a clue as to why, the first thing Sunday morning, Maria Munisteri had been banging on her husband's childhood friend's door, crying her eyes out and claiming that her spouse was in mortal danger because of a nasty slit in a vest.

"*No capish*," he said as plainly as he could.

Apparently, he was finally speaking her language, for she began to tell him the whole story:

Undoubtedly the most exhibitionistic event of the Sicilian social calendar is a wedding. On these occasions, the members of the wedding party strut around in exquisite, made-to-order outfits before hundreds of invited guests, all of whom are uncommonly knowledgeable about the art of fine tailoring. Why, most inductees, functionaries, and relatives of the Cosa Nostra can assess the craft of another man's suit at a glance, appraising each dexterous stitch and appreciating the sartorial *tour de force* inherent in any tailor's most challenging task: the shoulder, from which more than twenty individual jacket parts must hang in precise yet fluid harmony.

One of Tony's most demanding customers was none other than New York's most notorious Prohibition-era *mafioso*, known to friend and foe alike simply as "the Boss." A month before his daughter's wedding, the Boss had entered Tony's shop to be measured for his "father of the bride" suit. He had brought with him a bolt of the most elegant wool gabardine, a French import so finely woven that it felt like cashmere.

As fashion-conscious as they come, the Boss knew his body's twelve principal measurements by heart. His savvy sense of style told him just what kind of tailoring he needed. For example, he had instructed Tony to cut the shoulders extra wide in order to deemphasize his hips. His trousers, he had insisted, were to feature triple pleats at the waist and numerous other special touches and details of flair intended to flatter his rather corpulent figure. And no less important, the drape of his coat had to be ample enough to accommodate a holstered pistol — inconspicuously, of course.

At ten o'clock on the morning of the wedding day the Boss was to pick up the finished product. Only afterward would Munisteri breath easily; until then, Tony and his crew of tailors devoted their full attention to satisfying the *mafioso*'s exacting specifications.

Everything was proceeding apace until the Saturday night before the fateful, final fitting. Just as Tony was examining and reexamining the trousers, his ten-year-old apprentice (a neighbor's son he had been bulldozed into taking on even though he was a blithering idiot) got hold of the workroom's fabric shears — the ones with the twelve-inch blades — and wreaked havoc upon the Boss's brand-new suit.

This incompetent young menace should have been restricted to sweeping the floor, about the most challenging undertaking he could handle. But instead he was wielding the shears delinquently, trimming threads around the seams, when suddenly, almost with a will of their own, the scissors cut a five-inch-long incision right through the vest.

When Munisteri became aware of the damage, he stood silent and shaken for several minutes, mourning his own death. At first he even thought of telling his patron the truth and offering up the guilty apprentice as a sacrificial lamb to be dealt with appropriately. But several extenuating circumstances precluded this plan, not the least of them being that the youth was distantly related to the Boss's son-in-law-to-be. Furthermore, it was manifestly clear that the crime committed was too serious for a juvenile offender to take the rap, even if he was a walking advertisement for stiffer child-labor laws. No, only the life of a master tailor could atone for the death of his masterpiece.

There was neither the fabric nor the time to remake the vest before the Boss came for his fitting. Accordingly, Tony did the only thing his self-preservationist instincts told him to do: he ran for his life. Before his hasty retreat, he instructed his apprentice to wait in the shop and inform the don that Tony had had to leave early in the morning to attend an out-of-town funeral.

That was the story. Now Wikler understood, but he still didn't understand how he could help.

"I wan' you gonna speaka the Boss," Maria pleaded.

Remarkably, Sam agreed. Despite his extensive legal training, however, he had no idea how he might appeal such a sentence. He also had no idea how to locate the appellate division, but in this regard Maria had come prepared. Sam was to go to a candy store several blocks east and north, she said, and tell the soda jerk that he wanted to speak to "the Boss."

Sam considered the situation for a moment, asked Maria to leave the suit with him, and escorted the potential widow to the door.

Within an hour Sam had worked out a line of defense. It was risky, but considering the alternatives it seemed the only viable option.

"Shaindel!" he called out to his wife. "Please bring me my best three-piece suit and a needle and thread..."

Half an hour later, Sam was heading for shul and then for Munisteri's shop.

At 10:00 on the dot, the don and his heavy-metal entourage entered Munisteri's premises. The young perpetrator was there to greet them as arranged, apologizing for his master's absence.

"He'sa gone to a... a f-funeral," the boy stammered.

A few eyebrows were raised but the Boss wanted to get on with the fitting; he had a busy day ahead of him.

Carefully he removed the suit trousers from their hanger and stepped into the dressing room. A minute later he emerged, sliding his hands in and out of the pants' pockets to test their capacity and comfort. He then waddled over to the three-sectioned mirror and a smile snaked across his scarred, ugly countenance as he admired his triptych reflection from various angles. By his side at all times, the Boss's bodyguards vigorously nodded their approval.

Next he turned his back to the mirror and tried on the vest and the broad-shouldered jacket. Inhaling as he buttoned up his waistcoat, he could not resist running his hands over the silky-smooth fabric. "*Perfetto!*" he pronounced with satisfaction.

But when the don spun around to get a better view of himself, his face became redder than his waistcoat lining. His eyes bulged grotesquely from their sockets, a vein throbbed high in his forehead, and a bloodcurdling, ear-splitting bellow rent the air.

"MUNISTERI!" he yelled, but the blithering idiot quickly responded that Tony had left for a funeral.

All of the henchmen quickly peeked around their boss to get a look at his triple reflection and their jaws dropped. There before their astonished eyes, flying up from the bottom of the vest to both lower pockets was a row of embroidered, pink butterflies.

"MUNISTERI!" the Boss roared again, his mouth contorted in fury. It seemed that if he held his rage in any longer, he would blow his teeth out. The idiot apprentice reminded him yet again that Tony was at a funeral, but the don just hissed, "The nexta funeral he go to, he'lla be lyinga down!" And just to make himself perfectly clear, as his entourage stormed out of the shop, the Boss called over his shoulder, "Tella Munisteri to getta ready for a dippa in the Easta River!"

At 10:15 Sam Wikler entered the candy store to which Maria had directed him and told the man at the fountain that he wanted to speak to the Boss. The proprietor sized him up, spat out a wad of tobacco, and told him to come back at twelve o'clock.

Sam returned at noon. The "candyman" pointed to the last phone booth at the rear of the shop.

"But I don't know his number," Wikler protested. The man behind the fountain moved his head slightly to establish perspective and then landed Wikler a flat, you-stupid-or-something? look.

"Genius," he sneered in a dialect that anyone not from New York's Lower East Side would never understand, "youse don't call him, youse gets called." The soda jerk had a charming habit of rolling his eyes when someone didn't under-stand him, acting as if that person were an alien from a remote, uncivilized planet in a late-developing galaxy.

"Oh," Sam responded meekly. He stepped into the phone booth and sweated for twelve minutes. Then the phone rang. When he lifted the receiver, a voice said, "Yeah?" as though Wikler had called *him*. It was amazing: he'd re-ceived a call from an anonymous stranger and before he had even opened his mouth, he was already in the middle of a conversation.

"I need to see the Boss — urgently!" Sam implored.

Silence. After about a minute, which felt like an eternity at least, the voice told him to go to the barber shop of the Em-pire Hotel at 3:00 sharp.

In those days, every fancy hotel was equipped with a swank restaurant and an equally ritzy barber shop. Little did Wikler know that they serviced only the most exclusive clientele.

Sam entered the Empire Hotel's beautifully appointed lobby — a spacious, carpeted plaza surrounded by a richly veined marble counter that functioned as a reception desk. He veered into a velvet-covered tunnel of deep red, at the end of which was a gilt-lettered sign indicating that the restaurant was to the right and the barber shop to the left.

The minute Sam opened the frosted glass door, neither the parquet floor nor the violin Muzak floating down from the ornate ceiling could convince him that he was anywhere but in the depths of the lion's den. Every chair in the shop was taken, but only one gentleman was having his hair cut.

The sight was oddly comical. Beneath their fedoras, sundry gangsters sat in padded chairs — sans barbers — with odd-shaped protrusions jutting out from beneath the white capes covering their underworld figures. The chairs alongside the magazine rack were also taken by their comrades-in-arms, quite literally, who made little effort to conceal their hardware.

A fellow at the door asked Sam his name and what he wanted. It was all too obvious that this was the last place in the world anyone would go for a haircut. Without hesitation Wikler recited his name and request.

The doorman jerked his head toward the solitary figure having a trim, a middle-aged man with a hot towel around his neck and a huge Cuban cigar between his pursed lips. The barber stood on the side, stropping his razor.

Sam walked over to the Boss and waited another eternity until his presence was acknowledged.

"Well?" the don said at last, never opening his eyes.

For a brief moment, Sam contemplated the components of this bizarre reality. He had pleaded cases in the appellate court, in the Supreme Court, in the circuit court, and even on the tennis court, but never had he been awarded such outrageous indifference. Why, a judge could be disbarred for such behavior!

Suddenly Sam realized that it was all

for the best, however, and he reposi-
tioned himself ever so slightly so that if
the Boss deigned to grace the attorney
with either a direct glance or an oblique
look into the mirror, his view would be
blocked.

"Tony Munisteri's wife came to see
me this morning..." Sam began, waiting
for a response. But when not even a
grunt was forthcoming, it dawned on him
that there was to be no give and take,
and that for whatever time was allotted
to him he had the floor.

"She was very upset," he continued.
"A mother of three, as you know, she's
afraid something is going to happen to
Tony... I couldn't get out of her what the
problem was, but I would hate to see any
harm befall her husband. I've known him
all my life. We grew up together on the
same block. He was always an honest
boy and a hard worker."

Sam paused a moment to choose his
words carefully so that they sounded
moderately credible. "You know, you look
to me to be a reasonable man, and I'm
sure that you, too, would hate to see a
good guy get punished unjustly."

There was still no response from the
Boss. The Mafia don remained in the

exact same moribund pose he had assumed since Sam had entered the shop.

Wikler continued to try and arouse compassion for Maria and her children, to no evident avail. Obviously the Boss hadn't gotten as far as he had by being a pushover. And just as obviously, Tony was deemed unpardonable.

Nonetheless, Sam plunged ahead. He reshuffled his sentences, attested to the marked man's character, suggested an error had been made, and pleaded for clemency — all the while feigning ignorance of the crime committed.

There is a limit to how long one can talk to a wall, however — or, for that matter, to a partially concealed face with the lights off. Sam had far surpassed that limit. But just when he thought he could filibuster no longer, the Boss excised the cigar from his lips and muttered, "What's Munisteri to you?"

"Just a friend. But a friend is forever, with all the obligations and responsibilities that entails. I've believed that all my life."

"But you don' know what he done."

"I don't know what he *could* have done. He's not involved in any illicit activity. He's only a tailor."

"A tailor!" the Boss spat out in disgust as though the term were caught in his larynx. He still hadn't opened his eyes.

"A tailor indeed, and one of the very finest!"

"You don' know what he done," the Boss reiterated, chanting the words like a mantra.

"I've been saying that all along," Sam conceded, trying to steer the conversation in his direction.

"Tonight'sa my daughter's wedding," the Boss exhaled after an exceedingly long drag on his cigar. "It'sa bigga affair, I gotta looka my best. Friends, family, they come ina from every district. I thought I givva Munisteri a break, givva him a chance to lay his hands ona some good material and earna a few bucks. But he'sa wrecked what I givva him. Imported all the way froma France, just enough for a three-piece suita, and the blockhead goes ahead anda wrecks it!"

"Oh, I'm sure Tony can fix it," Sam said, sounding conciliatory and under-standing.

"No-o-o, I'ma gonna fix *Tony*; the dope isa dead meat." The Boss still hadn't opened his eyes, and Sam began to wonder if he ever did. The don took another long, contemplative drag on his cigar and then added, "He shoulda be having his feet fit fora cementa shoes righta now."

Considering the Boss's temperament and the way he settled scores, Sam realized that his own life might be in jeopardy. Furthermore, his audience with the don — and his chance to stay Tony's execution — was just about over. He had to make his move now!

Samuel J. Wikler, Esq., took a deep breath, closed his own eyes, and reached for his trump card. "I just can't believe that Tony could make a mistake in his craft," he stated authoritatively. "He is simply the *maestro*!"

That did it. The Boss opened his eyes and stared in disbelief at the profile of a Jewish attorney wearing his most elegant suit.

"Now that'sa nice suit," the Boss commented, as if to highlight his own misfortune. Sam drew nearer, yet he did not face the don directly. Fingering Wikler's lapel, the head of Crime, Inc., inspected the fabric and was duly impressed.

"Where you getta this?" the Boss

asked. "You think I could havva one made up for my daughter's wedding thisa evening? I make-a them an offer they can't refuse."

"Are you kidding?" Sam immediately regretted his choice of words but he forged ahead with his plan. In a minute at the very most, he would know if all his years of studying human psychology would reap dividends. "Such a suit has to be ordered months in advance. You can't even get anything like it over here; it comes from Saville Row — that's in London, you know. The closest approximation is what Tony can do..."

Sam then rotated his body for the Boss to get a full view of him and the don's cigar dropped from his lips.

"*What is that?*" The Boss aimed an accusatory finger at the lawyer's waistcoat.

"What is what?" Sam responded, feigning total innocence.

"That, *that!*" The Boss propped himself up in his chair and removed the hot towel from his neck to get a better look.

Sam looked up and down, pretending not to see what the Boss was referring to. "Oh, oh, *les papillons*. Don't tell me you don't know what these are! Why, every well-tailored suit has embroidered butterflies. They're a status symbol, a real touch of class! There is simply no better mark of a high-quality garment."

Silence reigned in the Empire Hotel barber shop as the clock on the wall ticked away two full minutes. When the Boss finally snapped his fingers, everyone jumped, startled out of their astonishment. One of the henchmen sitting near the door leaped to attention.

"Yes, sir, Boss," he said, almost saluting.

"Call uppa Vinnie," the don ordered, "and tella him to call offa Munisteri's fitting."

Heard from: Dr. Meir Wikler

Farewell to K'vod HaTorah

fter enduring the hardships of trans-atlantic passage in steerage and the humiliations of Ellis Island, thousands of Jews poured into New York monthly until, by the turn of the century, they accounted for over a quarter of the city's population. These Jewish immigrants were the classic greenhorns.

Three distinct types characterized the teeming masses. Perhaps the most prominent group were the *shvitsers*, the hustlers driven by the desire to discover gold in the streets of America. Having jettisoned their cargo of Jewish observance long before they docked, they felt no commitment to tradition, only to getting ahead. And get ahead they did, advancing from sweatshop workers to managers, from subcontractors to contractors, from jobbers to manufacturers, from peddlers to shopkeepers, from retailers to wholesalers. Entrepreneurs, their sole interest was in making money, and within a generation they emerged as the *alrightniks*, satisfied with their accomplishments and acquisitions.

Then came the radical free thinkers, who wished to transplant their political ideology to America. Socialists, anarchists, and various combinations thereof, they came with ideas and ambitions shaped by the tyranny of absolutism and pogroms, and viewed America through the distorted looking glass of eastern European politics. Obsessed with theoretical questions that were thoroughly irrelevant to the new world, they could arrive at no consensus regarding the nature of the revolution to come. So they rallied around their shared disdain for the so-called "clericalism" of traditionalist Jews, ridiculing mitzvah observance and instituting Yom Kippur balls and other public mockeries of Judaism.

The last group of greenhorns were

the observant Jews themselves, who endeavored to transplant their time-honored practices and professions into their new milieu. Shunning the sweatshops, which operated on Shabbos, these immigrants preferred peddling from pushcarts. By 1888, they had established over 130 different congregations in New York.

These pious Jews looked around and saw themselves surrounded by exactly what their *landsleit* had predicted: a *treife medinah*. *Chilul Shabbos* was rampant and Jewish education was at a nadir, with *kashrus* — its level of supervision pathetic — all but unobserved and assimilation already in high gear. Something had to be done.

Against the advice of those who understood the New Country better than they, the religious leaders naively decided to introduce in America the system of the chief rabbinate which had proved so effective in Europe. This form of organization could ensure a unified body to promote and direct religious observance and monitor the community's functionaries.

The proponents of the plan expected to finance the learned chief rabbi they would import from Europe by imposing a nominal tax on kosher meat. The very idea that a chief rabbi could operate authoritatively in the chaos of New York's uncontrolled freedom revealed how green these activists were.

Such an institution, subsidized by an unpopular tax, had indeed been the practice in eastern Europe, where it had worked mainly because the *kehillah* had functioned under governmental authority. In the "old world," the kosher meat industry had not been rife with corruption and scandal, or difficult to regulate or supervise.

Nonetheless, supporters of the plan gamely hammered out a constitution governing the rabbinate, which gave the chief rabbi absolute control over all religious matters. Specific guidelines were drafted concerning the issuance of *hechsherim*, one of the thorniest problems to be tackled.

Selecting a chief rabbi to enforce these by-laws was by no means a facile endeavor, but at least there was unanimity in purpose and resolve. There was but one search committee and a united consensus of every congregation in New York supporting its work.

While history bears dramatic testimony regarding the Providential emergence of our nation's leaders, one cannot help but wonder: what compels gifted individuals to assume these positions?

Certainly not ambition, for any leader of a Torah community is by definition a paragon of modesty and most scrupulously avoids the limelight. Only one steeped in Torah values and imbued with a genuine love for his people can ever be the rabbi of a community, especially a community like New York.

No one fit this description better than Rabbi Yaakov Joseph. A brilliant disciple of the Volozhiner yeshivah, Rabbi Joseph possessed a saintly personality and powerful oratorical gifts.

His reputation obviously preceded him, for the day Reb Yaakov Joseph arrived in America — July 7, 1888 — bore all the trappings of a holiday. An enormous crowd, clothed in their festive attire, traveled to the port in Hoboken, New Jersey, to greet the chief rabbi. After this royal welcome, the assemblage escorted him all the way to his tastefully appointed new home at 263 Henry Street on New York's Lower East Side. The pomp and circumstance, however, were disarmingly ephemeral.

One might imagine that New York Jewry would have hailed the arrival of such a distinguished and beloved figure from the old country. Yet instead of showering him with garlands, groups without and within the traditional community began to assail and vilify a man they had never spoken to or even seen. No sooner had Rabbi Joseph unpacked his bags than the Anglo-Jewish press, controlled entirely by irreligious and even anti-religious elements, began spewing forth a torrent of furious condemnations.

Undaunted by his detractors, Reb Yaakov Joseph immediately set about achieving the objectives for which he'd been hired. His first goal was to improve the abysmal *kashrus* supervision in the slaughterhouses. Needless to say, ritual slaughterers and butchers alike resented Rabbi Joseph's interference. So did the residents of the Lower East Side, who were asked to pay a nominal tax to subsidize new *kashrus* supervisors. Joining in the protest were the rabbis who had lost their income when Rabbi Joseph and his *beis din* had pronounced their *hashgachos* unreliable.

As though the actual *kashrus* of the meat were irrelevant, the opposition contended that America was the "land of opportunity," and that this fanatical foreigner had no right to deny its citizens their prerogatives and privileges. In due time, the penny surcharge on certified-kosher chicken was dubbed "*karobka*," the Czarist government's tax on kosher meat. Once this emotionally charged accusation had been leveled — conjuring up all the evils and persecutions the immigrant community had escaped from — reasonable discussion was impossible and the rabidly anti-religious press jumped into the fray feet first. Reb Yaakov Joseph was denounced as a scoundrel who delighted in bleeding poor widows and orphans with a tax levied only for his own gain and that of his wealthy patrons.

An *ad hominem* smear campaign (there isn't a more delicate term) was initiated, spearheaded by an association of butchers actively supported by the rabbis whose *hashgachos* had been rescinded by the rabbinate. Since the goals of the association had been clearly enunciated, its members had no reason to employ subtle tactics; their verbal assaults were explicit and direct and no holds were barred.

As this special-interest group was fir-
ing away, other factions began to plot
and scheme. Jews of primarily Galician
and Hungarian origin, for instance,
claimed that the chief rabbinate was
unfairly controlled entirely by Litvaks, as
Reb Yaakov Joseph and all his *dayanim*
were from Lithuania. The chief rabbi
himself was willing to compromise on
this point, but his overtures were re-
jected out of hand. Instead, without regard for the grave consequences of its
actions, the Galician/Hungarian con-
stituency hastily appointed their own
chief rabbi. In a disastrous domino ef-
fect, the chassidim subsequently followed suit, squelching all hope of city-
wide Jewish unity.

By now there was no longer even a
modicum of meaning or dignity left to
the office of the rabbinate. Notwithstanding, even after the rug had been
yanked out from under his feet, Reb
Yaakov Joseph continued to weather the
storm, remaining a paragon of self-re-
straint and self-respect.

No matter what perfidious new
charge was hurled at Rabbi Joseph —
and the assaults were virtually limitless
— he refused to stoop to the same

shameless mudslinging that typified his opponents. Both in public and in private, he would not speak out against his detractors, and he even forbade his supporters to brand as *treif* any meat not slaughtered under his supervision (although its *kashrus* was dubious at best).

But as much as Rabbi Joseph tried to rationalize and excuse his critics' unpardonable behavior, his generosity was never reciprocated.

When the rabbinate attempted to levy a modest tax to offset the expense of supervising the production of matzah meal, Rabbi Joseph's enemies considered this the last straw. At less than a quarter of a cent per pound of matzah, this tax was minuscule, but it was rich fodder for the press and the mobs eager to do away with the chief rabbi once and for all. Whatever dwindling support Rabbi Joseph had retained now withered entirely and the rabbinate's sponsors found that they could no longer afford to pay him.

In a bitterly ironic twist of fate, Reb Yaakov Joseph was reduced to working as a simple *mashgiach* for the butchers of New York. Bereft of his title and an object of scorn, he eked out a living until 1895, when the butchers discontinued his salary. Thus Reb Yaakov Joseph, the pious scholar, kosher-consumer advocate, and tireless activist for Torah education and observance in America, was left penniless and without any source of income.

Remarkably, the avalanche of degradations failed to break the rabbi's proud spirit, but it did take a heavy toll on his health. Soon after he was robbed of his livelihood — and decades before the advent of Medicare or medical insurance — the former chief rabbi suffered a stroke that rendered him bedridden for virtually the remainder of his relatively short life.

What felled the office of the chief rabbinate and chipped away at Reb Yaakov Joseph in the process? One can point to several factors, but chief among them lies the inalienable American right to self-assertion, which was at loggerheads with *k'vod haTorah*. As the country that provides so many downtrodden peoples with the hope of an egalitarian life, the U.S. was hardly the place for a monolithic institution devoted to upholding the Torah's absolute standards. On the altar of personal freedom, *k'vod haTorah* was sacrificed, and with it this princely champion of Torah ideals as well as untold millions of Jewish souls that would never know or identify with their heritage.

How apt, then, that America's foremost symbol and prime victim of *b'zayon haTorah* would yet provide a most inspiring affirmation of *chashivus haTorah*.

After years of confinement, isolation, and virtual abandonment by New York Jewry, Reb Yaakov Joseph regained the faculty of speech claimed by his stroke. This was truly cause for celebration, and Reb Yaakov Joseph could think of no more appropriate a way to articulate his gratitude than by delivering a *drashah* on *Shabbos Shuvah*.

Word spread that Reb Yaakov Joseph would be giving his first public lecture since New Yorkers could remember and attendance promised to be extremely high. After all, even the butchers could not deny (although the press certainly tried) that Rabbi Joseph was the finest orator in America.

Beis HaMedrash HaGadol on Norfolk Street, the largest shul on the Lower

East Side, was packed to capacity a solid hour before the lecture was to begin. Hundreds were denied entrance but remained outside nonetheless to catch a glimpse of the ailing rabbi. As the mobs swelled, police were even called in to maintain order.

Approximately an hour later, slowly and feebly, Rabbi Joseph hobbled up to the very podium from which he had addressed a crowd of similar size upon his arrival fourteen years earlier. Now as then, a hush fell upon the assemblage, with everyone straining to hear every word.

But it was not the same Rabbi Joseph who had addressed them years before. The man who had stood before them then had sacrificed everything to travel to the new world and establish a new order in America. Now the speaker was the victim of those who had opposed that order.

"*Shteit in Rambam*," America's greatest scholar began. Then he fell silent. Everyone craned his neck to catch the rabbi's next word, but it was not forthcoming. After a little while, the venerable rabbi's soft eyes filled with tears and his body heaved as he wept uncontrollably.

When he finally regained his composure, he uttered his very last words ever to be delivered from the pulpit.

"Do you know what it is for me," he whimpered between sobs, "to forget a Rambam?" Unable to remember the quotation upon which he wished to base his address, the great *gaon* — luminary of Volozhin, *maggid* of Vilna, and apple of Reb Yisrael Salanter's eye — stepped down from the podium and sadly made his way home.

A more important address has yet to be delivered on the North American continent.

What was it that destroyed Reb Yaakov Joseph? Not the constant abuse and the daily insults; not the spurious accounts of his policies in the press; not even the ruthless butchers and their partners in sin. No, the inability to remember the words of the Rambam was the ultimate disgrace for the tzaddik who had countered abuse with respect and ignorance with scholarship. This was the monumental lesson in *chashivus haTorah* that Reb Yaakov Joseph managed to impart before his holy soul was summoned to the Heavenly Assembly.

We shall never know which Rambam

Reb Yaakov Joseph had wished to quote at his *shiur*. But if the choice were ours, a meaningful citation would be the Rambam's inclusion of the laws of *k'vod ha-Torah* in his section entitled *Talmud Torah*, for quite simply, respect and honor for the Torah and its teachers is part and parcel of Torah learning and observance.

But if America's Jews were unable to bestow *k'vod haTorah*, they certainly knew how to bury it. On 24 Tammuz 5662 (July 28, 1902), Reb Yaakov Joseph died in his home on Henry Street. No doubt with a keen sense of guilt and remorse, the rabbinic leaders who survived him ruled that, in order to ensure proper respect for the deceased, the funeral should be delayed until July 30th to enable Jews from afar to attend. In the interim, New York's various congregations shamefully vied with each other for the honor of interring the rabbi in their shul's graveyard. His presence, they figured, would increase the value of the neighboring plots.

Mourners thronged to New York's Lower East Side from all over Jewish

America. Travelers from as far away as the Midwest as well as trains from up and down the eastern seaboard were crammed with people wishing to finally award Reb Yaakov Joseph the respect that he deserved. The United Orthodox Rabbis of America estimated the size of the crowd at over 100,000 people, making it the largest funeral that New York had ever witnessed.

Despite this grand scale, everything progressed in an orderly fashion — until the procession passed the large printing press factory of R. Hoe and Co., on the north side of Grand Street.

Near the corner of Sheriff and Grand streets is a triangular park formed by the acute-angled intersection of Grand and East Broadway. As the funeral cortege neared the park, the procession consolidated into four solid blocks following the hearse and its accompanying carriages.

The assembled advanced very slowly, not only due to the solemnity of the occasion but because they were inhibited in their progress by the multitudes of awestruck bystanders who sought to touch the hearse as an act of veneration. When the procession reached the park, it came to a virtual — and fateful —

standstill.

The employees of R. Hoe and Co. were mostly Ukrainian immigrants noted for their vitriolic and frequently vented anti-Semitism. Consequently, when they looked out their windows, they were seized by an overwhelmingly insatiable craving for Jewish blood.

It did not take long for their devious minds to concoct a diabolical scheme to turn the funeral into an even more mournful occasion. The workers swiftly amassed every lethal-looking piece of debris on the premises and took up their positions. Then, in an unprecedented action taken on the shores "inhabited in order to establish justice, insure domestic tranquility, provide for the common defense, and secure the blessings of liberty for ourselves and our posterity," a hail of fist-sized, iron nuts and bolts and a torrent of water from a fire hose rained down upon the defenseless masses.

The bedlam and confusion caused below generated great revelry and glee above. As scores of maimed and freshly wounded Jews lay soaked and bleeding on the street, some of their fellow mourners sought immediate retribution.

Umbrellas were thrust through the windows of R. Hoe's ground floor while others availed themselves of heaps of stones and broken bricks from a nearby construction site. But the moment the mourners commenced their counterattack, the police on hand descended upon them, inflicting terrible beatings and arresting scores of innocent individuals.

As the police continued to bash heads and shout insults, the assault from above continued unabated, with the "missiles" becoming more and more deadly. In the chaos, the coffin was dropped as thousands sought refuge or vainly attempted to fight back. Eventually, the water that had drenched everyone below was shut off and, as a parting shot, the fire hose itself was tossed out the window and into the battered crowd.

Miraculously, the peaceful character of the cortege was eventually restored as the mourners regrouped to continue escorting Rabbi Joseph on his final journey. Along the way, however, police reserves who had been summoned from adjacent precincts arrived and deemed it only appropriate to make their presence known. Unexpectedly, and without any provocation, the policemen charged at the crowd, wielding clubs and hurling epithets as if they were in collusion with the employees of R. Hoe and Co.

The survivors, now about 25,000 strong, finally made it to the cemetery, where they laid Reb Yaakov Joseph — and the idea of a chief rabbinate in America — to rest.

Although Rabbi Yaakov Joseph only received the respect he deserved on the day he set foot on American soil and the day his body was interred in it, his passing inspired two important expressions of *k'vod haTorah.*

First, on the night after Reb Yaakov Joseph's funeral, America's greatest rabbis — who had traveled to New York expressly for this occasion from New Haven, Rochester, Boston, Pittsburgh, Cleveland, St. Louis, and elsewhere — swelled the ranks of those convening to discuss the plight of Torah education and mitzvah observance in America. The result was the inception of *Agudas HaRabbonim.*

Second, New York City enacted an ordinance mandating that a policeman be present at every funeral in New York City to maintain law and order.

The abominable behavior of the police at Rabbi Joseph's funeral was censured in an investigation commissioned by the honorable Mayor Seth Low. But to this day the presence of a police officer at every funeral is not, as most people imagine, to direct traffic; it is a tribute to the great tzaddik who sacrificed his life for *k'vod haTorah.*

Heard from: Dr. Meir Wikler

GLOSSARY

Glossary

The following glossary provides a partial explanation of some of the foreign words and phrases used in this book. The spellings, tenses, and definitions reflect the way the term is used in *The Best of StoryLines*. Often, there are alternate spellings and meanings. Foreign words and phrases translated in the text are not included in this section.

ARBA'AH MINIM — the four species used during SUKKOS services

ASSERES YEMEI TESHUVAH — lit., the ten days of penitence; the ten days between ROSH HASHANAH and YOM KIPPUR

BACHURIM — unmarried yeshivah students

BARUCH HASHEM — lit., the Lord is blessed; thank God

BEIS DIN — a Jewish court of law

CHAMETZ — wheat, barley, spelt, rye, or oats leavened by contact with water

CHANUKAH — eight-day holiday commemorating the Jews' victory over the Greek Syrians and the rededication of the Temple. A MENORAH is lit every night of the holiday

CHASHIVUS HATORAH — the importance of Torah

CHASSIDIM (CHASSIDIC) — devout followers of a REBBE

CHASSUNAH — (Yid.) wedding

CHAZZAN — cantor

CHILUL SHABBOS — desecration of the Sabbath

CHOL HAMOED — intermediate days of SUKKOS and PESACH

CHUMASH — set of the five books of the Torah; any one of these five books

CHUPPAH — wedding canopy; the wedding service

DAYANIM — judges who preside over a BEIS DIN

DRASHAH — sermon

ERETZ YISRAEL — the Land of Israel

ESROG(IM) — citron, one of the ARBA'-
AH MINIM

GAON — genius
GUTT SHABBOS — (Yid.) lit., a good
Sabbath; Sabbath greeting

HAGGADOS — books containing the lit-
urgy of the SEDER and retelling the
exodus from Egypt
HALACHIC — pertaining to Jewish law
HECHSHERIM — certifications of KASH-
RUS

KALLAH — bride
KASHRUS — the Jewish dietary laws
KIDDUSH — sanctification; prayer recited over wine to usher in the Sabbath and festivals
KOHEN — male descendant of the
priestly family of Aaron
KOSEL — the Western Wall, the last remaining wall of the Temple courtyard
and an eminent holy site
K'VOD HATORAH — respect for the Torah

LANDSLEIT — (Yid.) people from the
same city or area
LATKES — (Yid.) potato pancakes tradi-

tionally served on CHANUKAH
L'CHAIM — lit., to life; traditional toast
LITVAKS — Lithuanians
LULAV(IM) — palm branch, one of the ARBA'AH MINIM

MAGGID — preacher; recognized preacher of the city
MASHIACH — the Messiah
MATZAH(OS) — unleavened bread
MAVEN — (Yid.) expert
MEHUDAR — beautiful; HALACHICALLY perfect
MENORAH — eight-branched candelabrum kindled on CHANUKAH
MINYAN — quorum of ten adult Jewish males, forming the basic unit of community for certain religious purposes, including prayer
MISHNAYOS — the earliest codification of Jewish oral law, compiled by Rabbi Yehudah HaNasi
MITZVAH(OS) — Torah commandment

NEILAH — the concluding service of YOM KIPPUR
NIGGUNIM — melodies

PESACH — Passover
POSKIM — HALACHIC authorities

REBBE — chassidic leader

RIBBONO SHEL OLAM — Master of the Universe

ROSH HASHANAH — holiday marking the beginning of the Jewish year

ROSH KOLLEL — dean of a post-graduate yeshivah composed of married students who receive stipends

S'CHACH — all-natural roof of a SUKKAH, commonly made of branches

SEDER — festive commemoration of the exodus from Egypt, conducted on the first two nights of PASSOVER (or the first night alone in ERETZ YISRAEL)

SHABBOS — Sabbath

SHABBOS SHUVAH — lit. Sabbath of return; the Sabbath between ROSH HASHANAH and YOM KIPPUR and marked by a lengthy, scholarly discourse on repentance

SHAMASH — light used to kindle CHANUKAH lights

SHEVA BRACHOS — the seven benedictions recited at a wedding and in the presence of the newlyweds during their first week of marriage

SHIVAH — lit., seven; the seven days of mourning, mandated by HALACHAH, following the death of a close relative

SHLEP — (Yid.) drag, haul

SHMURAH MATZOS — MATZOS guarded since the harvest, lest they become leaven

SHTEIT — (Yid.) says

SHULCHAN ARUCH — lit., set table; the code of Jewish law compiled by Rabbi Yosef Caro

SIMCHAH — joy, celebration

SIMCHAH SHEL MITZVAH — joy of fulfilling a MITZVAH

SIMCHAS BEIS HASHOEVAH — SUKKOS celebration reminiscent of the Temple festivities during that festival

SIMCHAS YOM TOV — holiday joy

SUKKAH(OS) — temporary dwelling inhabited on SUKKOS

TALLIS — four-cornered prayer shawl with fringes at each corner, worn by men during morning prayers

TREIF(E) MEDINAH — lit. unkosher state; nickname for America prior to the immigration of Orthodox Jews after WWII

TZADDIK — lit. righteous one; pious and saintly individual

TZEDAKAH — charity

YESHIVAH — academy of Torah study

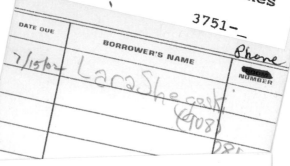

Library
Princeton Jewish Center
435 Nassau Street
Princeton, NJ 08540